HANDBOOK OF PSYCHOLOGY

BY

JOHN H. EWEN, F.R.C.P.E., D.P.M.

*Late Psychiatrist and Lecturer in Psychological Medicine, West-
minster Hospital, and Medical Superintendent, Springfield Mental
Hospital. Formerly Examiner in Psychological Medicine, Royal
College of Surgeons, England*

LONDON
SYLVIRO PUBLICATIONS LTD.
19 WELBECK STREET, W.1

—

1950

HANDBOOK OF PSYCHOLOGY

PRINTED IN GREAT BRITAIN BY
ODHAMS (WATFORD) LTD., WATFORD

PREFACE

This work is intended for students and practitioners who may be taking up the study of psychology for the first time. It represents an attempt to give an account of the more essential principles involved with their practical implications. The book has been primarily written for students working for the Diploma in Psychological Medicine and, towards this end, a section has been added dealing with the more important relationships of normal psychology to psychological medicine.

The author's task has been one of selection and emphasis and while the more academic aspects of the subject have been briefly depicted, an effort has been made to relate them to practical considerations and to modern opinions in a subject whose literature has become increasingly prolific.

A short bibliography has been appended in which acknowledgments are made to a number of works which have been consulted.

CONTENTS

5

CONTENTS

SECTION I

NORMAL PSYCHOLOGY

CHAPTER I

THE SCIENCE, SCOPE AND VARIETIES OF PSYCHOLOGY

SCIENCE AND PSYCHOLOGY

A science is coherent and unified knowledge classified and arranged under general rules and comprehensive laws which have been elaborated by the methods of scientific investigation. The physical sciences deal with material facts and processes, logic is concerned with the distinction between truth and error, ethics inquires into the possibilities and reasons for right and wrong willing, aesthetics deals with the constitution of the distinction between beauty and ugliness, ontology or metaphysics attempts to give an account of the nature of the universe. Psychology utilizes the methods of scientific investigation to formulate and systematize knowledge regarding mental life and its states and processes.

Psychology is, therefore, a science and no longer a branch of metaphysics. It now, however, becomes necessary to define of what psychology is the science and here difficulties are encountered because of the wide variety of definitions, none of which being entirely satisfactory. To call psychology the science of the mind implies the presence of an entity, the mind, as distinguished from the brain. Psychology has been defined as the science of consciousness but this is inadequate since unconscious processes have much influence upon mental life. Psychology has been called the science of behaviour but here again behavouristic reactions do not constitute the total subject of study and the importance of the rôle played by consciousness is disregarded. Stout defines psychology as the science of the processes whereby an individual becomes aware of a world of objects and adjusts his actions accordingly. Here account is taken not only of the subject but also of the object since subjective states and processes cannot be adequately described without reference to their objects. But the essence of psychology lies in the process of knowing, not in what is known, with the process of willing, not with what is willed, with the process of being pleased or displeased, not with what is agreeable or disagreeable.

Hence in psychology subjective and objective have a specialized meaning. Under subjective is included the relation which the mind has to its objects in minding them, the state, functions or acts of willing, wishing, attending and behaving. While wishing or thinking of a purpose is subjective, the purpose itself is objective since it is the mind's object and is what is meant, intended or thought of by the mind. Sensations are objective being parts of the total object before the mind. Because the past mental history is different in different individuals the objects which exist for the consciousness of one individual is different to those existing for another although all other conditions may be similar. Therefore psychology must study perceptions and conceptions, hopes, fears, and desires together with the objects with which the mind is concerned.

Psychology deals with psychical states and processes the modes of their occurrence and their objects. It is therefore the science of mental life or the science of the conscious and near conscious activities of living individuals and is concerned with modes of consciousness as connected within the unity of consciousness. It is the function of the psychologist to assume the psychological point of view the point of view of the spectator not concerned with passing judgment upon the subject's actions but seeking to understand the mental processes at work and to arrive at a true explanation and evaluation of their causative factors. Psychology is the study of human nature in its mental aspect and the elucidation of the motives that form the mainsprings of action lies in the province of psychological investigation and research. Psychology aims at providing a systematic and co-ordinated account of the laws and conditions of the life history of individual minds.

MODES OF CONSCIOUSNESS AND IMMEDIATE EXPERIENCE

Modes of experience or modes of consciousness are the relations of the mind to the objects it apprehends. All modes of experience form part of the conscious self and the unity of consciousness is displayed in purpose and its fulfilment, desire and its satisfaction, expectation and disappointment. All knowing, wishing, behaving and sensation are modes of consciousness and become absorbed into the conscious self. Modes of consciousness form part of a complex whole and while a material thing is composed of material things the conscious self does not contain conscious selves. Fragmentation of consciousness does not normally exist and thought, feeling, volition, purpose and recognition all fall within the unity of the same consciousness.

When a mind apprehends objects immediate experience takes place. The immediate experience is a mode of feeling and the immediate experience of one mind is particular to that mind and, while the physical object can be shared with other minds, the sensations or modes of feeling are individual and may be continued as a mental picture in the absence of the physical thing. A similar process takes place in hallucinations and in dreams.

Presentations are immediate experiences that are primarily objective and Berkeley held that presentations exist only in the mind. Presentations direct the flow of thought to objects which are not presentations and influence the apprehension of all other objects either directly, as immediate experiences, or indirectly, by mental dispositions. The vague state that surrounds mental images are amorphous presentations or halos surrounding the presentation. James pointed out the significance and value of the image lies in its halo.

DATA AND METHODS OF PSYCHOLOGY

It is clearly evident that mental states and processes are obviously connected with bodily behaviour. In other words, mentality is teleological or directed towards the achievement of ends. Mental life functions towards a purposive aim although the goal may not be clear and the means of achieving the purpose may be indeterminate and frequently conditioned by unconscious motives and factors. While the order of the material world is basically mechanical human mentality is fundamentally social and its implications must be considered in the community setting. Where the controlling interest is social, common sense must play a predominating rôle in the evaluation of psychological processes. Hence introspection as a method of psychological investigation, although of considerable value, does not suffice when dealing with the more complex mental processes. Introspection or subjective observation is defined by Locke as the notice which the mind takes of its own operations. In introspection as an instrument of psychological analysis there is a separate discernment of the self with an implied special development of explicit self-consciousness. The implicit consciousness of the self must inevitably influence the explicit. Introspection formed the basis of scholastic psychology and true introspection is not speculation but should be a direct observation of fact.

It is pointed out that the introspective process consists of a fundamental change from the objective to the subjective viewpoint which is followed by a stage of reflection during which the introspective process is concerned with the working of the subject's own mind. Here, however, if results are to be obtained, there must be control and direction by interest in psychological theory. This stage cannot usually be considered as scientific but introspection practised as a scientific method yields results especially in answer to questions of theoretical importance. Necessary adjuncts to true introspection are impartiality, attentiveness, training and practice. Methodical and systematic reflection directed by theoretical interest has evolved a conception of psychology that has thrown much light upon the study of sensation and it has been well said that the introspection of one generation starts the introspection of the next.

Introspection as a method of study has several inherent difficulties of which one of the most important is that of language since, as language is primarily a mode of communication, it is inadequate to describe mental experiences while the very act of introspection in itself tends to modify the experience. Again some experiences, particularly of emotional value, cannot be reproduced by the introspective process. Meaning, which is acquired by association and retentiveness cannot be introspective, moreover the mind has been evolved for the practical purpose of dealing with the external environment to which mental interest is primarily directed. This being the case, introspection is rendered more difficult and difficulties are also increased when introspection is carried out over long periods since the attentive faculties have to deal with not only the object to which introspection is directed but also with the mental operation itself. Complex introspection becomes in reality retrospection because of the time factor involved.

Objective observation as a method of psychological investigation consists of the study of the manifestations of mental processes taking place in others. The interpretation of the external bodily signs shown by others is carried out on the analogy of the observer's own experience. Objective observation observes the conditions and occasions of experience and directs its study to the behaviour of animals and children and to the reactions of adults under controlled circumstances as in the carrying out of the many mental tests that have been elaborated for special purposes. The method of objective observation is also used largely in the study of the abnormal psychological processes which display themselves in the symptomatology of mental disorder, delinquency and behaviour disorders in children.

It will be noted that in objective observation it is in many cases the behaviour of the object of study that is observed. Confusion between the objective observation of behaviour as a means of study and the behaviourist school of psychology should not arise since the cardinal tenets of the behaviourist school are the application of the principles of conditioned reflexes to psychology and the elimination of introspection as a method of investigation. Objective observation as a means of investigating mental processes was practised long before the concept of behaviourism was formed and while the introspective method was formerly regarded as the only method of adequate psychological enquiry it would be most unwise to neglect introspection as a means of study and entirely exclude it, as behaviourism does, as a mode of psychological research. On the other hand it must be emphasized that the physiological approach to psychology has received a very considerable impetus from the outstandingly successful results of physical methods of treatment in the psychoses. In psychology, as in any other science, dogmatism is to be deprecated and it is only by exploring every approach to the problem of mental life that psychological knowledge will advance.

VARIETIES OF PSYCHOLOGY

Psychological medicine is primarily concerned with the study of abnormal mental processes occurring in the psychoses, psychoneuroses and other maladaptations to the internal and external stresses. The crucial problem of mentality is to deal with inner conflicts and necessary adaptations to environmental circumstances. The capacity for adequate adjustment is the predominating feature of the well-integrated mind but where adaptation fails, maladjustment of the personality make their appearance and become the symptoms and signs of mental disorder. The study of abnormal mental processes therefore is of considerable aid in the elucidation of normal psychological functions and it directs enquiry towards the basic function of mind which is to understand and control the environment. Full control and understanding are rarely possible hence the necessity for increasing adaptation which normally results in mental development and further complexity of mentality with increasing growth of the personality. When adaptation fails or when the capacity for adaptation is unable to expand the unity of the personality, the integrity of mind and the harmony of mental processes are disrupted. The principles of psychological medicine are of particular value in explaining the rôles that the emotions and strivings play in mental life and psychopathology forms a most useful adjuvant to the study of normal psychology.

Experimental psychology forms another method of investigating mental life. Here experiments are carried out under controlled conditions. Its use, however, is more or less limited to the study of memory, learning and behaviour and to the psychical states produced by sensation. It is of value in measuring the duration of mental operations and in the estimation of physiological concomitants associated with psychological processes. Comparative psychology and its extension, correlative psychology, which gives a double comparison as in the comparison of the weight of the brain with intellectual ability, are of but limited value in human psychology since the conclusive factor is not brain weight but the quality of the cerebral cells. Comparative psychology compares the actions of people, classes and species and tabulates differences and similarities.

Genetic psychology as a mode of psychological inquiry is concerned with the mental growth of the individual and of the race. Here the extension of mental development is investigated and primitive reactions are followed to their complex and continuously extending horizon. Allied to genetic psychology is the study of child life, the behaviour of children and the development of the child mind. Educational factors are of importance in this branch of inquiry and it is here that behaviour is a guide to mental growth.

The examination of instinctive behaviour is exemplified best in the study of animal life where the instincts are uncontrolled and the resultant behaviour is not modified by educational or social factors. Ethnology, the study of the customs, beliefs and behaviour of uncivilized man is a fruitful source of psychological knowledge and its study has been of much assistance in assessing the origin and growth of social, ethical and moral principles.

The varieties of psychology form the main branches of psychological investigation. In general psychology the laws of the science are tabulated and described and principles are laid down that are applicable to psychology as a whole. Genetic psychology is a special branch that is concerned with the psychological aspects of heredity, mental development and the mental similarities and dissimilarities displayed, for example, in twins. The transmission of abnormal mental traits and the hereditary factor in mental defect form an important aspect of this branch. In applied psychology behaviour is predicted by tests and the life situation may be advantageously controlled as a result of psychological testing as in industrial psychology where the value of psychological research into the conditions and problems of industry and production is becoming increasingly evident as is also seen in educational and vocational psychology. Differential psychology attempts to evaluate the differences between individuals exposed to the same conditions and seeks to understand the causative factors at work that are responsible for differing reactions under identical circumstances.

Sociology or social psychology deals with the individual as a member of the social group or community. Here the individual is considered as a unit within the group and is investigated in his social relations and in the part that he plays within his environmental setting. In sociology the adaptative functions are of importance whereas in psychology the individual personal trends form the subject of study. Sociology is collective while psychology is individual but much may be learned regarding individual psychological reactions when the added stresses of community life are imposed.

A science becomes exact and accurate when it deals with measured quantities and this is the special province of experimental psychology in which reaction-time experiments and investigations into fatigue have yielded much knowledge of practical use.

Within recent years considerable advances have been made in the construction and elaboration of instrumental aids to the acquirement of scientific knowledge and psychology has benefited by the use of electro-encephalography which provides a method of investigating psychological phenomena in their relationship to cortical activity. The interdependence of psychological and physiological processes has long been recognized and electro-encephalography may well provide additional data of value in estimating the relative importance of the theories of psychophysical parallelism and interaction.

Electro-encephalography assesses the electrical activity of the brain and action potential changes that are reproduced and amplified can be seen and recorded as oscillations. Berger has demonstrated that these potential alterations are due to the electrical activity of the cortex and these potential waves are recognized as the Berger rhythm or Berger's alpha waves. During sleep the electrical activity of the cortex is changed and the alpha waves are replaced and interpolated by delta waves which are of a lower frequency. Similar changes of rhythm may also take place in mental disorder, epilepsy and hypoglycaemia.

It is probable that further investigation with the aid of electro-encephalography will throw more light upon the relative importance of psychological and cerebral processes and upon their bearing on mental life.

The theoretical conceptions of the Gestalt school of psychology may have far-reaching influence upon the science of psychology particularly in the relationships of psychological processes to cerebral activity.

CHAPTER II

BODY AND MIND. KNOWING, STRIVING AND FEELING

BODY AND MIND

Common experience indicates the interdependence of physical and psychical processes, the primary connection between psychological manifestations and neurological occurrences and the influence that psychological phenomena have upon the organic bodily life.

The primary feature of the existence of mind as a distinct entity and in no way to be confused with brain is common ground in the two hypotheses which seek to explain the more exact relationship between the two entities. As Stout emphasizes, the function of the central nervous system is to control and combine the various processes which are continually happening in the body but psychical processes *per se* are only connected with the grey matter of the cortex. McDougall well states that no confusion should exist between mind and brain and that the fundamental function of the mind is to guide bodily movements. Mind is the resultant of mankind's efforts to control and understand the environment and the concept of mind has been elaborated from the facts of behaviour and of experience. The outward expressions of mind are the marks of behaviour. The mind "experiences" and the general form of experience is to think, as Descartes said, *cogito ergo sum*. The mind experiences sensations, appreciates their meaning and dictates conduct according to its strivings, interests and purposes. It will be noted that the appreciation of sensation is not enough to determine conduct. The mind aided by preformed mental dispositions adds meaning and it is the meaning that controls the ensuing behaviour.

There are two theories of the relationship between body and mind, psychophysical parallelism and the theory of interaction. It is clear that psychical processes have, as their immediate material, correlated cerebral processes although the nature of the correlation is indefinite. Stout treats the connection as one of concomitance and concomitant variation. In other words, when a certain psychical process occurs a certain cerebral process occurs simultaneously with it. Variations in the psychical process are attended by variations in the correlated cerebral process. In brief, the psychical state comes into being coincidentally with the cortical disturbances but the psychical processes are not derived from the correlated nervous processes.

This is the theory of psychophysical parallelism and it may be said to cover the known facts fairly adequately. It forms a good working hypothesis and is the orthodox view and is supported by metaphysics. On the other hand it does not explain the occurrence of consciousness and it might be held to be at variance with modern psychological theory which has some grounds for supporting the rival theory of interaction.

The theory of interaction states that the mind and body are both independent entities each capable of influencing and being influenced by the other. The mind interacts with the body and the body with the mind. Objections to the theory that the mind influences the body spontaneously of its own initiative are that it involves a contradiction of the law of conservation of energy. Should it be argued, however, that the mind is a form of energy, mental energy will interact with physical energy. But against this it is a principle of natural science that all forms of energy are mechanical and the introduction of a new form of energy —mental energy—conflicts with the general and accepted concept. The implications of interaction are that the mind shapes and uses the brain as an instrument in the achievement of its own interests. Here conscious life is an independent factor controlling and modifying nervous impulses.

It must be pointed out that in any theory of the relationship between body and mind the principle of conscious striving after ends must be recognized. The mind determines bodily conduct from the data that results in meaning and the ensuing behaviour is directly co-ordinated with the mind's conscious purposes and strivings. The theory of interaction recognizes that all human behaviour is purposive—the attribute which forms the essence of mental activity and which is an expression and manifestation of mind. Hence there must be postulated the necessity for mental energy to carry on mental processes.

It has previously been indicated that modes of experience are the relations of the mind to the objects apprehended. A main factor in the elaboration of mental experience is the neurological factor of the sensory nerves transmitting the afferent impulses to the brain. These physical factors are therefore imperative in the production of modes of consciousness and a postulated interaction simplifies the mechanism involved.

Again, it is a cardinal tenet of psychological medicine that mental disorder may be produced by purely psychological processes, but modern treatment such as insulin therapy and electroplexy has shown that physical treatment profoundly alters abnormal mental processes and since the theory of interaction postulates the brain as being the organ of the mind the interdependence of physiological and psychological processes receives further support.

COGNITION

Since the time of Kant there has been three ultimately distinct modes of being conscious of an object. The cognitive mode, the mode of affection or feeling attitude and the conative mode.

Cognition is the presentation of an object to consciousness. It is the fact of knowing or recognition which is characterized by an attachment of familiarity. Simple apprehension, however, is not the only factor in cognition in so much as the question of belief and doubt logically involves judgment since to think of a thing is not the same as affirming or denying its existence. Simple apprehension itself is the imaginative attitude as in phantasy in which the mind abstains from the reality principle and from the questioning attitude and hence the passing of judgment does not arise. Cognition, therefore, involves the two factors of simple apprehension and judgment since it is impossible to judge without apprehension while the fact of knowing is inevitably blended with some degree of judgment.

Cognition, therefore, includes all modes and degrees of being cognizant of an object and the word object, in its relationship to cognition, means whatever the mind can be aware of. Stout differentiates between object and presentation. Under object is included the total whole with which the attentive process is concerned and which consciousness is endeavouring to cognize more fully and more distinctly. The term presentation is confined to the special characters or relations of the object as they appear successively in different phases of the cognitive process.

It has been indicated that cognition is made up of simple apprehension and judgment. To these must be added conation and affection co-operating in the process of being fully conscious of an object. Just as cognition is subdivided into two component processes so may conation and affect be considered under the heading of interest. Interest is striving or desiring together with the feeling attitude of pleasure or displeasure. Developing cognition indicates how interest may be satisfied while interest progresses towards its own satisfaction, hence cognitive development is dependent upon and connected with conative development, conation supplying the driving power, the striving and desiring, while cognition supplies to the process its determinate character. Conation is active, cognition is passive. Cognition allied to interest results in full consciousness.

CONATION

Conation is the felt capacity for striving. All willing, wishing, craving and desiring are conative impulses seeking satisfaction. It will be noted that conation is a felt capacity and therefore conation and its fulfilment cannot coincide in the same moment of consciousness since the conative impulse would be merged in its goal and would not be felt. Hence full satisfaction is delayed and may come by gradations each giving partial satisfaction only. In the operation of the so-called instinct of curiosity which, in reality, is an attitude of suspended judgment, full satisfaction may be impossible to achieve as in metaphysical speculations since the means of satisfying curiosity may not be available.

Conative impulses are characterized by great strength and continued persistence but may die from fatigue, disappointment or inability to reach their goal although conation may persist subconsciously and influence conscious behaviour. In the well-integrated mind conation persists over very long periods and the operation of conative trends are of considerable importance in the evolution of the personality.

Again belief in the reality of the self is largely determined by the strength and persistence of conation since the fundamental origin of the concept of the self arises in the production of effort.

The object of conation includes some change in the actual circumstances. The object of the conative impulse is its end, its end state of terminus is complete satisfaction. Therefore, the total object of conative consciousness consists of two parts, the means and the terminus. Striving for the means is necessary and therefore they form part of the object of conation. The terminus of conations is desired for its own sake. Where the means are indefinite the terminus must be uncertain. It has been well said that we know fully what we want only when we know how to obtain it. Without knowledge of the goal the conative impulses are undirected, ineffective and uncoordinated, a state which may develop into a psychoneurotic syndrome in which indecision, restlessness and infirmity of the will are characteristic symptoms.

On its path to satisfaction the conative process shows trial and error, success and failure, pleasure and pain.

Change in the actual circumstance is included in the object of conation, the change consisting of either something to be added or something to be removed. When the main emphasis is on the introduction of what is absent, conation is called appetition, the positive phase of the conative impulse. All aspirations, desires and longings are part of the positive phase. The negative phase arises when the emphasis is on the removal of what is actually present and here conation is called aversion. Forms of the negative direction of striving consciousness are antipathy, regret, hatred, dislike and repugnance.

Three levels of mental development are related to three levels of conative process. On the perceptual level conation is present as the perceptual impulse to immediate action resulting in bodily movement. On the level of train of ideas conation becomes desire. On the ideational plane of mental development the conative impulse is present as ideals. Here the terminus is perhaps speculative and certainly complicated, involving a complexity of factors and goals that have to be considered and attained gradually and with difficulty. The ultimate aim may be beyond achievement but can still be pursued. It is here, on the higher levels of intellectual development that the unity of conation is exhibited and the conative impulses become organized into unified systems. In conative unity the direction and nature of striving becomes more diffuse and each goal is pursued, not so much for itself, but as a means towards other aims, as an aid to the evolution of the self with the expansion of the personality which becomes a unified and organized system of conative tendencies forming part of a general life situation. It is in conative unity that mankind differs from animals who are creatures of detached and isolated impulses without unity of the self and, therefore, without personality. Conative continuity unites the strivings of the past, present and future in a cohesive whole from which emerges the concept of self and personal identity.

The intrinsic nature of conation is a subject upon which but little agreement is found. Conation has been defined as the experience of effort or endeavour in whatever connection it occurs. Sensations and affection form part of the conative impulse and it is held by some psychologists that they form the whole of conation. It lies within the province of introspection to elucidate as to whether there is always some immediate experience of striving or tendency towards striving and the difference between activity and the feeling of activity must be distinguished.

James held that conation is simply a special variety of kinaesthetic or motor sensation due to conscious or subconscious muscular action taking place during conative experiences. Then sensations derived from muscle, joint and tendon contractions are the experiences of striving. McDougall, on the other hand, maintains that the sense of effort in conation varies independently of muscular strength. Titchener affirms that introspection must be the final court of appeal. There is, however, but little doubt that conscious process always involves tendency towards an end and is hence intrinsically conative in character.

AFFECTION

Affection is feeling tone and is the consciousness of what is happening within the organism. It has been pointed out previously that one of the modes of being conscious of an object is by feeling attitude or affection and that interest is made up of conation and affection. Whatever furthers the conative impulse gives a feeling tone of pleasure, whatever hinders conation in the achievement of its aim yields a feeling attitude of pain. The term hedonic tone is used in the description of the relationships between conation and affection and it denotes the pleasure or pain involved in a mental process.

When an organism is stimulated the consciousness that the organism has of the stimulus is the affect, affection or feeling. A state of feeling is the most basic perceptible state of consciousness and it serves as an indicator of the effects of the environment upon the organism. No special sense organ is concerned in affection, which is a vague feeling tone which pervades mental processes and although it has quality, intensity and duration, it is not localized nor has it definite form.

Further variations of feeling attitude are found in the emotions and sentiments but in the emotions the feeling tone is specific and distinct from the hedonic tone while in the sentiments there is an organized system of emotional tendencies. Hedonic tone, however, is accompanied by physical changes whose character varies according to the results of conation. Conditions that further conation towards its goal of satisfaction give an affect of pleasure whose physical counterparts are seen in increased pulse rate and depth of respiration combined with increased muscle tone. Alternatively, when conation is impeded a painful affect is experienced showing itself in vasoconstriction, lack of muscle tone, diminished respirations, weakness of the voice and diminution of all the bodily secretions except the lachrymal.

Physiologically considered, conation seems to correspond to a disturbance of nervous equilibrium while satisfaction of the conative impulse appears to restore nervous equilibrium. A painful hedonic tone disturbs nervous equilibrium and continues to obstruct its restoration.

The theoretical point as to whether conation succeeds affection or is preceded by it has given rise to much argument. The school of Bentham and the psychological hedonists hold that conation is determined by affection and that the process is carried out in the order of cognition, affection and conation. The hormic theory postulates that affection follows conation, the order being cognition, conation and affection. This view is supported by Aristotle and Schopenhauer with Freud and James in opposition. Stout considers that feeling tone and conation coincide in time while McDougall holds that the probable order is cognition, conation, changed cognition and affection.

Marshall postulated in his theory of affection that the affect of pleasure is dependent upon a surplus of stored energy while displeasure is a feeling tone related to diminution or absence of energy. The theory has been criticized on the ground that it does not explain the pleasure and pain of perceptual and ideational activity.

Feeling tones of pleasure and displeasure form the backgrounds of consciousness—the conscious subjective state—and feeling of this type must not be confused with the emotions. Feeling tones are elementary or simple feelings whereas the emotions attached to the operations of instinctive activity are complex, more definite and specialized. The James-Lange theory of the emotions postulates that emotion is simply the organic sensations welling up within the organism. In the same way, the feeling tones of pleasantness and unpleasantness may represent a general organic condition but the differentiation in these feeling tones is not paralleled by a discernible difference in the organic state. The main fact, however, that emerges from introspection is that the conscious processes of pleasantness and unpleasantness are the same with whatever other mental processes they are connected.

CHAPTER III

INNATE AND ACQUIRED TRAITS.
SENSATION AND SENSATIONS

An organism may be defined as a collection of tendencies made up of natural or native tendencies and acquired tendencies. Natural native or better inherited traits are derived from the parents, from the remote ancestors and, as Jung has demonstrated, from racial factors. The history of an individual goes back to the beginnings of human life. The infant displays native reaction carried out by its sensory, muscular and neurological equipment. As growth continues these reactions become more complex and the natural intelligence expands together with the inherited impulsive and emotional traits. The acquired traits are dependent on the native tendencies and are the results of the adaptations that the individual makes to environmental conditions.

Native mental activities are instinctive, emotional, affective, reflex and sensational. These are provided by the innate constitution. The impingement of the environment upon the inherited traits is the process of learning, of incorporating the new with the old and expanding and modifying the endowments given by nature in the light of the acquirement of the necessary adaptations to the environment.

Sensation is one of the native mental activities with which psychology has to deal and its study is of equal importance to that of the instincts, emotions, affections and the reflexes.

In the first place a distinction must be made between sensation and sensations. Sensation is the notice taken by the organism of the modifications produced by the stimulus. Sensation itself as a conscious experience is an abstraction since the total mass of sensations are experienced and not an isolated one sensation. Sensation provides the means by which attention must be directed towards anything that influences the welfare of the organism. Sensation also controls the growth of complex actions by their acquired meaning and preformed associations. A pure sensation cannot be experienced in its pristine purity except in the new-born child and only then for a short period since recognition follows sensation and recognition is, perhaps, the simplest and easiest learned acquirement. Sensation is a response to a stimulus which may be simple, as in the unicellular organism, or complex, as in the human being. It is clear that something must be added to sensation, something that is derived from past experience, something that supplies a meaning that the mind infers from the stimulation of the afferent nerves which transmit sensory impulses to the cortex.

SENSATIONS

Sensations unlike sensation are psychical states. They exist at the time they are actually experienced and are objects of the mind conditioned by the two factors of an internal or external sense organ and a stimulus. The intrinsic feature of sensations lie in the fact that the mind has a facility for impressional experiences of a certain kind. Muller's law of specific nervous energy lays down that a given stimulus on different end organs results in different sensations and that different stimulations of the same end organ results in the same sensation.

Knowledge regarding sensations may be briefly summarized as follows. They are immediate objective experiences or presentations which have no existence when the sensations no longer are sensed. Sensations are not complete and independent objects as it is necessary for something which is not immediately experienced to be apprehended in relation to the sensations. They, therefore, mean something beyond themselves. This meaning, conveyed by sensations, is dependent upon association and retentiveness. Thus any sensation must be associated with past experience. The Gestalt school of psychology, however, would criticize this view.

Stout has enumerated the intrinsic characteristics of sensations. Common to all sensations are the attributes of quality, intensity and duration. The quality of a sensation is dependent upon the rate of vibrations of the stimulus and upon this, intensity and duration depend. The attribute of extensity is found in visual and cutaneous sensibility. Extensity implies a local diversity of cutaneous and retinal areas which is independent of the nature of the sensation. Local sign is a further characteristic of visual, cutaneous and tactile sensibility. Local sign is an immediately experienced place difference probably depending on central nervous structures receiving impulses by way of the kinaesthetic nerves. Stout postulates that the perception of extension, form and spatial relations is conceived upon the basis of extensity and local sign. A further attribute of sensation is affective tone which depends upon the quality of the sensation and varies with its duration and intensity.

Ladd has pointed out that affective tone does not arise solely from quality, intensity and duration of sensation. To the special excitement produced by the sensation is added a diffuse excitement of the nervous system which arises from the sensation. This fourth factor is surplus excitation and it is probable that the varieties of pleasant and unpleasant feelings are conditioned by surplus excitation which is present, not only in relationship to the special senses, but also in relationship to the organic sensibility. Experimentally, alterations in respiratory movements during pleasant and unpleasant sensations are dependent upon surplus excitation.

The sensations may be classified under the headings of higher and lower, a division which takes into account the contrast between the intrinsic impressiveness of sensations and their value for perceptual consciousness. Where perceptual consciousness is highly organized sense experience becomes more differentiated. Touch, sight and sound are better discriminated than taste, smell and temperature and, therefore, are higher sensations while organic sensation remains the lowest on the scale. The lower senses arrive earlier in mental development and heat and cold, smell and taste are more primitive and do not show the fine discrimination displayed by hearing, vision and the cutaneous sensibilities.

A further factor in the distinction between the higher and lower senses is evident in the mode of combination into which the various classes of sense experience enter. The higher senses combine by colligation in which there is grouping or arrangement as in colours and there is a distinct presentation of any two combined senses. The lower senses combine by fusion or blending where the distinctive features of the individual senses disappear and the presentation of any two sense qualities become blended as in gustatory and olfactory sensibility.

A reflex act is an immediate motor response to a centripetal excitation. In the sensation reflex the stimulus which evokes or tends to evoke a reflex also gives rise to a sensation by which attention is directed towards the control of the reflex process for the purpose of safeguarding the organism. While the pupil reflex occurs normally without sensation the presence of a foreign body in the eye will not only cause contraction or dilatation of the pupil but there will be also a sensation of strong affective tone which arouses attention by its intensity and by its attached affective tone.

A further sensational experience is that of transition, which is displayed in vision and touch. Two points that may be stimulated on the visual or tactile field may be indefinite but, if moved, a well-marked sensational experience follows.

Of all sensations the most primitive is organic sensation. Organic sensation includes sensations due to the state of the internal organs of the body. The general feeling of well-being or ill-being is dependent upon the total collection of sensations arising from the organism. These states of common sensibility or the coenaesthesis are produced from the bodily organs and originate in the anabolic and katabolic alterations which are continually taking place. The primary stimuli lie in the vegetative condition of the organism and are concerned with the varying alterations in the bodily secretions, the blood-expiratory exchange and the processes of digestion and assimilation. Organic sensation corresponds to the general vital action of stimuli as distinct from their action on specially differentiated sensory organs.

The most primitive of the organic sensations are hunger and thirst and to these must be added such sensations as headache, nausea and suffocation. It will be noted that while the special senses have distinctness and localization, organic sensibility is vague, diffuse and lacks clarity. It may be that organic sensations are a result of blending of sensibility and that the process of awareness of the organism to them arises within the deeper layers of the mind.

The psychological importance of organic sensations lies in the fact that they affect the emotional attitude of the subject and also determine to a considerable degree the affective tone of special experiences as in sensations, perceptions and ideas. Their influence upon affective consciousness must therefore be reflected upon conative consciousness. Hence the stimulus in organic sensation may pervade other sensations by overflowing into other organs.

In abnormal mental states, changes in the organic sensations may give rise to delusional ideas as in involutional melancholia and dementia paralytica where changes in the organism are reflected and symbolized in the mental disorder. Again the organic changes in pregnancy and in tuberculosis are displayed in the symptomatology as in the spes phthisica of tuberculosis and the longings of pregnancy. Organic sensations are also factors in the evolution of temperament which, in turn, influences the growth of the personality and the individual's mode of reaction to life. Finally, organic sensations aid in the production of that continuous unity with the totality of sense experience on which the concept of the self is founded.

Kinaesthetic sensation or muscle, joint and tendon sensations is akin to the sensations of pressure and in ordinary experience the two sensibilities are joined and are only differentiated by an effort of analysis. This sense of bodily movement has its stimulus in the variable states of joint, muscles and tendons. The information conveyed by kin-aesthetic sensation is a meaning acquired by association (complication) with the special senses of sight and touch and is of much importance in the control of reflex and voluntary movement. Kinaesthetic sensations aid cutaneous and visual sensations in the perception of spatial relation-ships and in the appreciation of weight. In tabes dorsalis, a neurological disorder due to syphilitic infection of the spinal cord, ataxia and incoordination of muscles are characterized symptoms in the second stage of the disease when the motor neurones become involved, but in the beginning of the disorder, it is the sensory neurones that are first affected, resulting in impairment of muscle, joint and tendon sensibility.

In cutaneous sensation the skin is responsive to four different types of stimuli which result in the five unlike sensations of heat, cold, touch, pressure and pain. In addition, Myers has described diffuse light touch in the absence of touch spots.

The investigation of cutaneous sensibility has formed a fruitful subject for the application of the experimental method in psychology, particularly in tactile or pressure discrimination in which the perception of apartness is implicated. In Head's experiment, in which the radial and external cutaneous nerves were cut at the elbow and the cut ends joined, the main sensations derived from the peri-phery of the body were experimentally analysed by Head and Rivers who divided them into the deep and the cutaneous and subdivided the cutaneous into the proto-pathic and epicritic. Following suture of the nerves the first cutaneous sensations to return were those of pain, large differences of temperature and inaccurate localization. These sensations were termed protopathic. Later accurate localization, small differences of temperature and fine dif-ferences of cutaneous sensation became evident. These were called epicritic sensations.

It will be seen that the characteristics of the protopathic

sensations are diffuseness, strong appreciation of pain, lack of relative localization (compass test), appreciation of extreme of temperature and crude appreciation of extensity or diffuseness, while epicritic sensation is marked by much more discrimination and accuracy. Light touch and intermediate degrees of heat and cold are appreciated and relative localization or apartness is sensed. Hence for relative localization and appreciation of position, direction and shape, epicritic sensibility is imperative.

It is found, however, that in pathological conditions of the spinal cord and bulb there is loss of relative localization associated with loss of muscle, joint and tendon sensation or kinaesthetic sensation, but in these cases epicritic sensation is normal. It therefore follows that the perception of apartness, shape and size may be lost without defect in cutaneous sensibility. Hence the loss is due to central and not peripheral conditions and thus local sign, the immediately experienced diversity of places within an extensive whole, is probably dependent on central rather than peripheral factors and the nervous impulses on which local sign depends follow the same path as the impulses from muscle, joint and tendons. It must be indicated, however, that where local sign is abolished, absolute as differentiated from relative localization may still be appreciated since there is a diversity in the local colouring of sensation. Local colourings are secondary or auxiliary local signs, although Ward postulated their identification with local sign, and cannot carry out the function of experiencing place difference which is centrally conditioned. Stout holds, however, that local sign is not the only factor in the perception of apartness, distance, direction, shape and size and that action movements with their attached kinaesthetic sensations must be adjuvants of importance.

It has been stated that organic sensation includes sensations due to the state of the internal bodily organs and that they are states of common sensibility originating in bodily alterations. In the same way fatigue is an organic state and often a conscious state.

Fatigue is a sensation or a complex of sensations and is a

diminution of muscular or intellectual power which has its origin in prolonged physical or mental activity. Fatigue, primarily an organic state, results in sensations of fatigue with a corresponding physical or mental proclivity towards rest which is the response to the organic need. Accompanied by a feeling tone of weariness or drowsiness there is a wish for rest or sleep. Muscular and mental fatigue terminate in the same sensations and in both the element of muscular strain is involved, the difference being one of degree. Predisposing factors in fatigue are age, physical condition and unsuitable work. In muscular fatigue the products of fatigue act as muscular toxins as can be demonstrated experimentally by means of muscle-nerve preparations. In mental fatigue the capacity for mental work as estimated by the ergograph is either increased or greatly diminished.

It is necessary to distinguish between fatigue and exhaustion. In fatigue there is muscular pain with increased pulse rate and deeper respirations. The cutaneous arterioles are dilated and there is profuse perspiration with diminution of body temperature and mentally, impairment of attention and memory with ideational confusion. In exhaustion there is cardiac palpitation, dyspepsia and vertigo. Mentally, irritability accompanied by auditory and visual hallucinations are prominent.

Experimental work by means of the ergograph has shown that short periods of rest are beneficial but the picture is obscured by the emotional attitude of the subject and, as Myers has pointed out, the personal factors are of individual importance.

An increased capacity for work both muscular and mental is given by caffeine and this drug does not obscure the presence of fatigue. The use of alcohol in the elimination of fatigue shows considerable individual variations and frequently is detrimental to the quality and quantity of the work performed.

CHAPTER IV

ATTENTION, PERCEPTION, ASSOCIATION

Consciousness in its cognitive aspect is concerned with the fact of knowing. In all states of knowing there are two principal factors, the subjective and the objective. The subjective factor is the personal factor, the individual perceiving or thinking. The objective factor is the object perceived or the image which is thought of. The relationship between the mind and its object is influenced by attention, an activity which determines the cognitive process. Hence attention may be defined as the attitude assumed by the subject during the cognitive process. This attitude of attention is a primary feature in all mental life and is essentially the concentration of consciousness on some particular sensation or object.

This attitude of focusing consciousness upon one particular object amongst other objects, upon one particular sensation or image amongst other sensations or images, this absorption of one particular experience amongst other experiences is dependent upon the factor of attention which is derived from the selective activity of consciousness hence attention may be defined as interest determining cognitive process.

At any one moment consciousness is impinged upon by a great variety of stimuli of both internal and external origin. The field of consciousness then consists of two parts, the field of inattention and the field of attention. In the inattentive portion there is implicit apprehension, a vague state of marginal awareness which influences the general condition at the moment. In the field of attention, however, there is only one object upon which attention is focused at any one time since the unity of the attentive process is unity of interest and psychologically there is no

35

such thing as divided attention although of two apparently attentive processes one because of training or habit, may not require active attention, or, because of rapidly alternating attention between two objects a true active attentive process may be simulated. The same attentive process may, however, be concerned with a number of varying objects, providing that the objects are integral parts of the same whole.

Two varieties of the attentive process may be described. In voluntary attention the element of conation is involved since voluntary attention is directed towards some interest, aim or desire. Again, anything that serves as a stimulus to instinctive activity will excite attention. Voluntary attention differs from non-voluntary attention since, in the latter, there is no expressed volition to attend and attention is either enforced or spontaneous.

It will be seen that so far as the attentive process in the individual is concerned the factors of personal interest, desire and striving are of paramount importance. To these must be added the factor of habit of attention, the attentive process here depending on associations formed in past experience. The power that a stimulus has to determine attention is dependent upon its factor of advantage.

Factors of advantage are objective factors which are differentiated from the subjective factors enumerated above. The objective factors are concerned with the attributes of the object receiving attention. It is obvious that the nature and intensity of the external stimulus are of prime importance in the attentive process. Other objective factors in attention are the extension of the external stimulus as in advertisements in which it has been stated that the attention afforded varies as the square root of the advertisement space in question. The novelty of the external stimulus is clearly a special factor of advantage which stimulates the instinctive activities of curiosity and fear. Change and constant repetition in the external stimulus are outstanding factors in originating an attentive process, while size and change of movement of the stimulus are factors of advantage which are commonly experienced.

Again, a definite outline of an external stimulus attracts attention more than an amorphous shape. These factors of advantage are essentially the basis of the layout of advertisements and their appealing power to the observer is influenced by the psychological mechanisms.

PERCEPTION

In the preceding chapter, sensation has been defined as the notice taken by the organism of modifications produced by the stimulus. Sensation is the resultant experience of stimulation of the cerebral sensory areas. The mechanism here involved is physiological. Sensations, however, are not complete and independent objects and mind responds to a sensory impression not only by a sensory experience but also by an act of knowing, a knowing of the presented facts. In other words, the total response constitutes a perceptual process and sensation aided by the meaning which is acquired through the agencies of association, memory and experience, results in perception, that mental reaction that has its origin in sensation and its culmination in perception. Essentially, perceiving an object is thinking of it with the aid of sensory qualities and by amalgamating these qualities with memories, images and ideas, the total experience results in a percept. Sensation augmented by past experiences revived by association results in perception by means of a train of mental activity which may be fundamentally dependent upon the integrity of the cerebral sensory and motor association areas. The perceptual process is guided and aided by attention, conation, expectation and persistence.

It has been stated that perceiving an object is thinking of it by the aid of sensory qualities but in imagery or imagination the object is remote and actual sensory experience does not take place although the image is like a sense experience but is not conditioned in the same way. The image, therefore, is less distinct and definite and lacks detail.

The theoretical explanation of perception is a matter regarding which controversial issues have been prominent for many years and efforts to explain association by linking psychological processes with corresponding neural connections have resulted in much theorization and speculation. The law of neural habit postulated that the passage of a nervous impulse through a chain of neurones leaves that chain more or less permanently altered in such a way that its resistance to the passage of further impulses is in some degree diminished. In other words, it was assumed that frequent simultaneous excitation of two groups of cerebral cells resulted in a lowering of resistance and in an increased facilitation to the passage of impulses. To a considerable extent this theory was dependent upon the supposed exact localization of cerebral functions. Cerebral functional localization, however, is not so definitely determined particularly in relation to the association areas and the growth of knowledge regarding the electric potential of cortical areas has formulated a new method of approach.

Formerly, it was considered that the meaning conveyed by an image was dependent upon the stimulation of associative groups while the doctrine of the fringe of thought postulated that meaning was given to the image or sensation within the focus of consciousness by the mass of sensations or images within the stream of consciousness. The psychic-stimulus theory maintains that sensations and images are the stimuli which evoke meaning.

Modern views on the theory of perception discard the former concept of association tracts in which associated neuronic groups become habituated to facilitation and lowered resistance by experience and systemization. The Gestalt school advanced the view that mental processes cannot be subdivided into parts but must be regarded as physiological wholes or patterns which are not evolved by experience but which are innate. Gestalt postulates that mental processes cannot be broken up into component parts but must be evaluated as wholes and not as a totality of sensations. In perception, Gestalt holds that there is a mental capacity to perceive and know the complex wholeness of the group of circumstances. In brief, the present tendency is not to break up stimulus and response into

their separate parts but to assess them in their integrated
entirety.

REFLEX ACTION

Reflex action is an immediate response to a stimulus.
The conditioned reflex is obtained by a building up of
associations acquired by a combination of natural or unconditioned stimuli with stimuli with which the inborn
reflex has become associated.

The conditioned reflex is acquired by experience and
operates without the co-operation of intelligent consciousness and in the absence of the normal unconditioned
stimulus. The factor underlying the conditioned reflex
is association, associations dependent upon cortical
mechanisms.

Pavlov's experiments have demonstrated the importance
of the factors of conditioning, learning and the rôle played
by the cortex in association, but their results do not justify
the far-reaching conclusions which have been deduced from
them by some of the behaviourist school of psychology
who hold that the conduct of mankind is only the aggregation of conditioned reflexes. This theory ignores the conative impulse and the rôle that purpose plays in mental life.
That purposive action radically differs from mechanical
processes is implied in foresight and in the criteria of purpose as shown by the persistence, variation and retentivity
displayed in human behaviour. Purposive action forms the
basis of the hormic theory which postulates that mind is
expressed in purposive action.

Reflex action has been defined as an immediate response
to a stimulus and involuntary production of activity
dependent upon the integrity of the reflex arc. The response
may be muscular or glandular as in the knee jerk, pupillary
reflex, salivary reflex and many others. Reflexes may also
be of an inhibitory character. Unconditioned reflexes are
the simple, the co-ordinated and the convulsive reflexes.
The conditioned reflex, as has been pointed out, is acquired
by training and education and while reflex response results
from a normal stimulus it may also result from any

stimulus with which the normal stimulus has become associated. In the first case the stimulus is the normal or unconditioned stimulus, in the second case the stimulus is conditioned by association with the normal stimulus. This conditioned or secondary stimulus gives rise to a conditioned response which is dependent upon associations resulting from processes within the cerebral cortex.

Reflex action is inherent and not acquired and is a permanent involuntary response which operates without preparation in adjusting the organism to influences which affect it. Reflex action is fundamentally necessary to the organism as an innate mode of protection.

On comparing simple reactions with reflex actions it is found that the simple reaction is slower than the reflex and the response is arbitrary, temporary and requires preparation. The simple reaction is voluntary and conscious while the reflex is involuntary and often unconscious.

THE HORMIC THEORY

Previous references have been made to the hormic school of psychology and, in the study of various forms of action, purposive action must receive consideration. The essence of the hormic theory is that all human and animal behaviour is purposive and directed and elaborated towards a goal. This postulated urge to action is regarded as an expression of mind and has points in common with the libido of Jung and the élan vital of Bergson. McDougall is the premier exponent of the hormic theory and of the importance of purpose in mental life.

It is necessary to distinguish between conation and purpose. Striving or conation are comprehensive terms which may or may not be associated with purpose. Purpose implies conation but not all striving is directly purposive since foresight of the goal may or may not be present. It is, however, a cardinal point of the hormic theory that purposive action is regulated by a knowledge of the aims to which it is directed. Again the conative impulse is furthered or hindered by pleasure and pain. These affective attributes to conation, according to the hormic theory follow conation, the sequence of events being cognition, conation and affection. Psychological hedonism on the other hand holds that affection precedes conation. McDougall takes the view that the probable sequence is cognition, conation, changed cognition, affection. Whichever sequence may operate the fundamental tenet of the hormic theory is that purposiveness is essentially conditioned by mind, conation and purpose being inherent characteristics of mental activity and resulting from mental as opposed to physiological factors.

Here lies an essential cleavage in psychological theory and it is necessary to give due weight not only to the arguments on either side but also to the recent changes that have taken place in the concept of mind. Physiological factors are attaining an increased importance in psychology. The growth of physical treatments in mental disorder, the study of electric cerebral potential and the experimental results of what may be called the more moderate schools of behaviourism combine towards an elimination of the older faculties theories of psychology and towards a replacement of the former concept of mind by more mechanistic and organic entities. That the organism experiences is clear, that the mind is the sole experiencing agent is a postulate that modern psychological and physiological research is examining.

Purpose and conation, however, are obvious in the behaviour of animals and human beings and the hormic theory must be considered as a mode of approach to the elucidation of the factors involved. Purposive action according to McDougall is revealed by the marks of behaviour from which purpose is deduced.

The more extreme behaviourist schools hold that conditioned reflex action explains all animal and human behaviour, but McDougall points out that purpose is accompanied by experience, foresight and conation and that the criteria of purpose radically differs from the factors involved in reflex action.

The criteria of purpose are seven in number and may be briefly considered under the following headings.

(*a*) Purposive. Ending of movements when a particular change is accomplished. In animals, movements are in abeyance when change is brought about. It is held to follow that the movements are therefore purposive since the reflex does not seek a goal.

(*b*) Persistence. Activity persists even when the originating factors for activity are in abeyance. In reflex action behaviour continues only as long as the stimulus operates.

(*c*) Preparation. Purposive action prepares for the new situations and does not come to an end automatically. In reflex action no preparation is necessary.

(*d*) Spontaneous. Movements show spontaneity and are therefore purposive. Reflex movement requires special stimulation.

(*e*) Retentivity. The past tells upon the present. Experience improves future behaviour. Reflex action is not improved by repetition except in the conditioned reflex.

(*f*) Totality. The organism acts as a whole, a total reaction is shown. In the reflex the reaction is always partial.

(*g*) Variation. The direction of movements are constantly varied with ensuing variation in behaviour. In reflex action there is fixity and behaviour can be predicted.

It will be seen that according to the hormic theory behaviour may be divided into purposive behaviour and mechanical behaviour and that purposiveness is exhibited in the marks of behaviour and not in reflex action which is a mechanical and stereotyped response to the stimulus.

Simple reactions, reflex actions and purposive action have now been briefly explained. A further form of action may be distinguished in animals and human beings which is instinctive action.

Instinctive action differs from purposive action in so much as instinctive action is held by some observers to be without foresight nor is it markedly improved by repetition or retentiveness. Instinctive action is characterized by persistence and preparation and is varied in its efforts towards satisfaction and is altered by the results of experience. The primary points in instinctive action are its persistence and its inherent tendency to continue to seek a satisfaction that may be delayed. In comparing instinctive action with reflex action the difference lies in degree, the reflex being immediate while the instinctive action is prolonged, preparatory and complex since the achievement of its goal is more delayed and distant. The reflex is the response to the stimulus, instinctive action may in some cases be a response to an object acting as the key operating the liberation of instinctive action. Characteristic and individual to instinctive action are the primary emotions. Instinctive action is universal throughout life and is a form of action in which reason is not involved. In instinctive action the organism acts as a whole and while experience may modify its action experience is not necessary to the performance of that action.

The view that instinctive action is conative and purposive is held by McDougall and the hormic school. Purpose implies foresight of the goal whose achievement terminates instinctive behaviour. The rival theory is that instinctive action is simply a series of reflexes, the chain reflex operating without purpose, conation or knowledge of the end. The hormic school, however, would point to three marks of behaviour exhibited in instinctive activity, variation, preparation and persistence of activity in the pursuit of the goal and would hold that conation and purpose are thus involved.

CHAPTER V

INSTINCT

A science becomes more exact when the definitions of its subject matter are firm, concise and generally accepted. It cannot yet be stated that psychology fulfils these conditions and this fact is particularly prominent in the definition of instinct. It is, therefore, necessary to inquire into the context of the various definitions offered and as far as possible to assess their value and estimate their relative usefulness.

James defined instinct as the faculty for acting in such a way as to produce certain ends, without foresight of the ends and without previous education in the performance. The important factor here is the question of foresight.

Stout states, " to what extent we are to recognize the presence of instincts in human beings depends on the way in which we choose to define the term instinct." In addition, Stout points out that " if we insist upon the condition that to be instinctive an action must be perfectly performed apart from practice and prior experience, the term "instinct" will be hardly applicable at all to the activities of man and it will be unduly restricted in its application to the behaviour of the lower animals." It will be noted from the above that Stout considers that a wide gulf exists between instinctive activity in animals, insects and birds and instinctive behaviour in human beings and that what may be regarded as the operation of instinct in the insect and animal is difficult to correlate with instinctive behaviour in organisms higher upon the scale of development where instinct becomes more and more modified in its operation by learning, intelligence and experience.

Lloyd Morgan, in dealing with the instinctive activities

of organisms low on the developmental scale laid down the following criteria of instinctive behaviour. Primarily, the operation of instinctive activity does not involve learning, in other words, instinct is native behaviour. Secondarily, the instinctive activity involves the organism as a whole. Thirdly, the activity is of use to the species and is carried out by all members of the species. These criteria are operative for organisms low on the scale but as mentality develops instinctive activity becomes altered by learning and experience and hence human instinctive behaviour is changed and modified by acquired factors. Again, as has been indicated in the previous chapter, the advocates of the chain-reflex theory explain instinctive activity in animals as the resultant of accumulated responses initiated by a primary stimulus. This behaviouristic view of instinct is dependent upon reflex action but the more moderate behaviourists point out that reflex action results from a prompt response to the stimulus whereas instinctive activity is characterized by delay, persistence and preparation and is, in fact, a persisting tendency to reaction which must be regarded as instinctive and not reflex.

McDougall, the principal advocate of the hormic theory defines instinct as an innate psycho-physical disposition which determines the organism to perceive, to pay attention to, any object of a certain class and to experience in its presence a certain emotional excitement and an impulse to action which finds expression in a specific mode of behaviour in relation to that object. In this definition the operative words are "innate," "emotional excitement," "impulse to action" and "specific mode of behaviour." McDougall deals primarily with human instinctive behaviour and includes in instinctive action cognition, a knowing of the presented facts, conation a striving towards a certain form of action and affection, the experiencing of an emotion (affect) connected with the object of interest.

McDougall's views have received considerable criticism as also have his somewhat extensive list of instincts, latterly called propensities, and the rôle that emotion is postulated to play in instinctive activity. Purpose and conation form the foundations of the hormic theory which perhaps under-estimates the part that physiological factors may play in mental life.

In the theories of instinctive activity summarized above it will be seen that there is a considerable diversity of opinion. In human instinctive behaviour, however, the predominating factor is the undisputed fact of instinctive activity varying in degree and strength, originating in an innate propensity, uncontrolled in organisms of a low stage of development, controlled and modified in human beings by experience, education, social factors and adaptation. The essential difference between instinctive behaviour in animals and human beings lies in the modifying action of the growth of human intelligence and in the faculties of adjustment and adaptation to the circumstances of life. In addition, by the process of sublimation alternative aims are offered for the satisfaction of instinctive trends that are not available to organisms in which intelligence has not attained that degree of development which characterizes human mentality.

According to the hormic theory the main channel through which the vital energy is expended is provided by the instincts and the operation of instinctive activity is associated with the particular and individual primary emotion accompanying the working of the particular instinct. It is from the display of the appropriate emotion that the form of instinctive activity in action is deduced.

Instinctive activity is directed and influenced by sensation and hence attention and its continunity aggregates in conative unity, unity of desire and striving. Prime factors in human instinctive behaviour, according to McDougall, are variations in behaviour initiated by the results of previous behaviour, interest and learning by experience while the criteria of attentive consciousness are manifested in persistence, inquiry and investigation. The influences of previous experiences in instinctive activity ultimately coalesce and become generalized by transfer of association to new conditions and here reason is called into play as in the protective and parental instincts which form the basis of justice and morality. The inter-play of the twin factors of attention and continuity of interest influence learning by experience and hence particular associations and dispositions are formulated and meaning (psychic-stimulus theory) is acquired.

The hormic theory maintains that it is instinctive action and not reflex action that provides the explanation of human behaviour which is elaborated from innate tendencies in mankind and from which issues, aided by experience and education, the units of character. Stout emphasizes the importance of retentiveness in learning from experience, particularly in organisms high on the scale of development.

Amongst the methods used in psychological investigation the study of animal life is one of the most important primarily because it is in animals that instinctive behaviour is demonstrated in its native purity and because the instinctive equipment of animals is considerably larger than that of man. Further, animal psychology provides information regarding the instincts that throws light upon the more complex instinctive behaviour of man. It is, however, in the estimation of the rôle that purpose plays in instinctive activity both in animals and in man that animal psychology is of particular value. The hormic school maintains that purposive action can be deduced from the instinctive behaviour of animals and of man and that the operation of instinct is, to a varying degree, dependent upon intelligent consciousness. Again, instinctive behaviour normally originates by a complex activity of perception with which is associated the tendency to change and vary the nature of the means by which the goal is achieved. McDougall points out that any object that stimulates an instinctive response is like a key that unlocks a door. The perception of the specific object is the lock, the specific object itself is the key. The turning of the lock is not a mechanical process like a reflex since it involves persistence, variations of behaviour and learning from experience, in other words, the process shows the marks of behaviour characteristic of purposive action and also the

co-operation of intelligence. In addition, the factors of
motive, appetite and emotion are prominent and typical.
On the other hand, the more specialized the instinct is the
less is the demand for the co-operation of intelligence.

Hence instinct in man is a process of gradual development not specialized as in insects, birds and some animals,
but attended by an extended and varied facility and
demand for acquired adjustments of behaviour. Since
specialized pre-adaptation is absent in the instinctive
behaviour of man its place is taken by the faculty of learning by experience which is an outstanding attribute of
man's congenital equipment. It is, therefore, manifest that
the operation of instinctive activity in man is masked by
intelligence and acquired behaviour and hence the working
of the instincts are obscured by the added factors of learning, attention and interest upon which is superimposed the
gloss of civilization and culture. In addition, the instinctive
strivings of mankind are swayed by social factors and
altered by imagination, the use of language and the evolution of the sentiments.

On summarizing the more important factors of instinctive
behaviour, it will be noted that human instinct is a process
of gradual development involving the attributes of perception, attention, conation and emotion. The field of
instinctive specialization in man is not nearly so marked
as in animals and the influence of alteration and variety in
behaviour is typical. The innate factors of learning and the
operation of intelligence tend to obscure the mainsprings
of instinctive activity while the capacity for retentiveness is
an essential adjunct. In mankind the primeval instinctive
urges may find expression not only in an alteration of the
instinctive aim itself but also in variability and multiplicity
of the means by which the ultimate goal is achieved. The
instinctive striving of man in his community setting is influenced by his social structure, by the factors of reward
and punishment, by the elaboration of the sentiments and
by the repressive influence of morality, ethics, education
and collective opinion. Because of practical circumstances
and community standards instinctive activity constantly

requires sublimation and it is the function of psychology to assess and derive the individual repressions that may impede the outpouring of the libido, that vital urge which, if adequately satisfied, yields contentment, but which, if impeded, may result in mental disorder.

INSTINCT, EMOTION AND APPETITE

That a special mode of experience accompanies the working of the instinctive impulses is a cardinal feature of the hormic theory. According to this view the outward signs of the operation of any instinct is comprised of the signs of the appropriate emotion that is displayed. McDougall postulates that the primary emotions are guides to the particular instinctive activity in operation and are a peculiar quality of experience which is individual to each instinct. This view has received much criticism and it is clear that the James-Lange theory of the emotions is fundamentally implicated.

With regard to appetite the position is not so obscure. Instinctive activity is in abeyance when appetite is not present. It is only when the instinctive urge is stimulated by the two factors of appetite and perception of the specific object that the particular instinct gains its full domination over the personality and results in that train of activity that seeks to culminate in the satisfaction of an instinctive urge. Appetite is conditioned, to some extent, by the bodily metabolism but should internal factors be in abeyance the specific object does not excite the appropriate instinctive impulse and only an indirected and indefinite restlessness becomes evident. Here the mental perturbation lacks its outlet and instinctive trends seeking satisfaction become manifested in psychoneurotic or psychotic symptomatology since the impulse to action and overflow of energy is conditioned by the internal and external circumstances prevailing.

In this situation, Rivers postulated that the instincts operate in connection with the " all or nothing " law, either the excitement of the instinct at work is maximal and therefore urgently requires satisfaction or the instinct is in abeyance and therefore only results in an undirected and ineffectual striving since its satisfaction is not within consciousness. The marks of a free instinctive impulse are the attention which is given by the mind towards modes of satisfaction and towards the train of activity involved in the achievement of both the instinctive and the emotional goal visualized.

INSTINCT IN MAN

The operation of the human instinctive urge is obscured by the factors of intelligence and learning by experience. In addition, the faculty of retentiveness must receive consideration since the original equipment is somewhat indefinite and lacks variety. But in apposition to these disabilities the congenital dispositions of mankind are paramount. Dispositions result in a predictable mode of behaviour providing the mental activity of the individual concerned is accurately assessed. The factors of attention, specialized interest and learning by experience predominate in mental instinctive activity and result in a greater variety and a more diffuse instinctive equipment than that displayed by animals. Stout points out that the development of the human mind is dependent upon these qualities and that the paramount position of human mentality on the scale of evolution is attributable to these inherent dispositions.

Modern views on instinctive activity in man differentiate between the highly specialized instinctive behaviour of organisms low on the scale of development, for example, insects and the higher but less specialized instinctive equipment of mankind where the need and requirement for intelligence as an adjuvant to instinctive activity becomes essential.

In man the life situation is one of instinctive activity which may be overwhelmed by desire. The factor of advantage that man has over other mammals is that of imagination which practically issues in the aid given by the use of language the elaboration of the sentimental attitude and the direction of purpose towards its achievement. Here imagination plays a primary rôle since the imagined foresight of the future in its relationship to the past conditions spontaneity, initiative and continued effort all reinforced by the elaboration of the sentiments, the use of language and essentially by the mechanism of purpose whose fulfilment is dependent upon imagination.

It would appear evident that human instinctive striving is directed by the possibilities of reward and punishment, a phrase which may be condensed into the approval or disapproval of the community mind. This criterion, however, does not illuminate the true picture. In spite of what has been previously depicted, there is but little doubt that the conative impulses of mankind are influenced and directed towards the wish to realize in practice the inherent desire to achieve an ideal of character and conduct which has been laid down by the self and augmented by percept, example and education.

CLASSIFICATION OF HUMAN INSTINCTS

Many attempts have been made to enumerate the various human instincts but none is entirely satisfactory since a generally accepted definition is lacking. Some authorities hold that there are only three primary instincts, the sexual instinct, the instinct of escape and the gregarious instinct. These three primary instinctive urges are sometimes alluded to as sex, self and society. Other psychologists group the instincts under the three headings of responses to organic needs, responses to other persons and play responses. A further classification comprises the sexual instinct, the parental instinct, and the instincts of fear, aggression, curiosity, self-assertion and nutrition. McDougall gives a list of fourteen " propensities " which he regards as instinctive. His views have been criticized on the grounds that several of the impulses he described are not considered instincts by other psychologists. As, however, McDougall includes what is regarded as instinctive by other authorities, his list of instincts is given here for completeness.

(*a*) The Sexual Instinct or Instinct of Reproduction.

The sexual or mating instinct is characterized by universality, strength and intensity. The factor of appetite is well
seen in the working of the sexual instinct and here instinctive behaviour is only called into play when appetite is
present. Appetite is increased by the perception of the
specific object, normally an individual of the other sex or
the sex characters. The goal of the instinct is the act of
union. In some organisms the operation of the instinct is
marked by a seasonal variation and by periodicity.

McDougall points out that in the sexual instinct the
cognitive aspect of instinct is well marked since there is an
innate disposition to perceive and discriminate the secondary
sex characteristics. Here the perceptual aspect of the
instinct influences conation and affection. The working of
the sexual instinct is accompanied by the emotion of lust.

In comparison with other animals the sexual instinct in
man matures relatively late. McDougall's view is here
directly at variance with those of Freud, who maintains
that the working of the sexual impulse can be demonstrated
in infancy. The sexual instinct has affiliations with the
parental instinct, whose emotion of tenderness is conjointly
aroused with the primary emotion of the sexual instinct.
The instincts of assertion and submission also co-operative
with the sexual instinct in its working. The instinct of
pugnacity or aggression may likewise be aroused during
the operation of the sexual instinct, particularly when any
impediment results in delay in achieving the desired instinctive goal. Tenderness and the protective impulse of the
parental instinct are considered to be basic factors in the
elaboration of the sentiment of sex love. The sexual instinct
may, therefore, be classed as a chain instinct linking different instinctive reactions together, the original stimulus
being the sex characters.

The main channel through which the libido or vital
energy is expended is furnished by the instincts and
the potential energy of the sexual instinct may become
impeded in its discharge through its normal channels.
Hence alternative channels may be necessary for its expenditure. These are obtained by the normal process of

sublimation by which the libido is deflected into other channels. Hence, the sexual impulse, modified by ideals and sentiments, may expend itself in the appreciation of art, music and literature, and in the many opportunities of methods of sublimation that are offered by community life.

(b) The Instinct of Self-Preservation, Fear or Escape.

McDougall names this instinct the instinct of escape since self-preservation implies consciousness of the self and this is only present in an advanced stage of intellectual development.

The instinct of escape operates in two phases, a flight to shelter and remaining hidden over the period of time during which the instinct is operating. The instinct of escape takes its place together with the sexual and the herd instinct as one of the strongest of instincts. Its goal is escape or the avoidance of danger and its primary emotion is that of terror, fear, alarm or fright. In gregarious animals the first reaction that follows the stimulation of the instinctive impulse is often a cry, the cry of fear which is individual to the particular species. The key to the instinct is therefore noise.

The instinct of escape is most marked in its operation in those animals that do not have adequate means of defence, in which timidity in inherent and in which the aggressive instinct is poorly developed. The operation of the instinct involves a tendency to seek shelter amongst those of its own kind and here the herd instinct is conjoined. Minimum stimulation of the instinct results in the expressions of caution and fearfulness which, should the situation not be resolved, result in a state of terror and intense agitation with the display of the physical concomitants of fear. Should escape be impossible, efforts may be made to control the instinctive activity but the emotional concomitants tend to inhibit action and, therefore, conflict may frequently result.

In its extensions the instinct of escape is involved in the control of those impulses that may be at variance with social life and in the evolution of religious beliefs there is a joint action of the instincts of escape and curiosity.

(c) The Herd Instinct.

The gregarious or social instinct is of paramount importance in social life but this view is not held by some psychologists who deny that gregariousness results from instinctive activity. McDougall postulates nostalgia, or a fearing of loneliness or isolation, as the emotion accompanying the operation of the instinct and gives the instinctive goal sought as the wish for the near presence of other members of the same species. The advantages of gregariousness are clear. Collective defence and attack, mutual warnings of approaching danger and the pooling and sharing of knowledge and its benefits are obvious assets which accrue from the operation of this propensity. In human beings the herd instinct is an example of the co-operation of intelligence with instinctive activity, in animal psychology the facts are more contentious.

The operation of the herd instinct is strongly confirmed by habit and by that experiencing and sharing of emotion that is named by McDougall as primitive, passive sympathy.

The gregarious instinct is often associated with the operation of the instincts of escape, aggression and curiosity, it being sufficient for one of the latter instincts to be in operation to evoke the herd instinct. In its extensions the herd instinct helps to formulate the social structure with its customs, laws and institutions. It is responsible for the advantages of community life and is a prime factor in the evolution of civilization.

McDougall maintains that the genesis of active sympathy, a feeling of the same emotion, has its root in the gregarious impulse.

(d) Primitive Passive Sympathy.

Primitive passive sympathy is the capacity to be aroused by that kind of instinctive behaviour whose signs are displayed by others of the same species. It is held by McDougall that primitive passive sympathy is the basic form of sympathy in so much as it is a " suffering with "—the experiencing of any feeling or emotion when and because it is observed in other persons or creatures who express that feeling or emotion.

The operation of primitive passive sympathy is uniquely observed in the working of the gregarious instinct. While the instinctive goal of this instinct is the near presence of other members of the same species, it is necessary for complete satisfaction of the instinct that other members of the species should be experiencing, sharing and feeling the same emotion.

According to this view, primitive passive sympathy is the factor that renders gregariousness advantageous to the units within the herd and is the cement that holds the herd together to form the foundations for the evolution of organized society. The results of primitive passive sympathy within the herd are also manifested in panic and collective aggression. The relationship of primitive passive sympathy to active sympathy is causal, active sympathy being rooted in primitive passive sympathy. Primitive passive sympathy is also one of the chief factors in the evolution of the sentiments. Again, in the minor instincts of laughter, primitive passive sympathetic tendencies are counteracted by laughter.

(e) The Instinct of Combat.

The instinct of aggression or pugnacity is stimulated when there is obstruction or thwarting of any other instinct. The operation of the instinct of pugnacity is, therefore, conditioned by the frustration of other instinctive impulses. The stronger that the thwarted instinctive urge is experienced the quicker the instinct of combat is evoked by the obstructive process.

The instinct of aggression operates in two phases, the attitude of threatening and the phase of attack. The accompanying primary emotion manifested in the working of the instinct of combat is anger, rage or fury in ascending progression. The goal of the instinct is the removal of the obstruction. Particular stimuli to the evocation of the instinct are obstructions to the food-seeking instinct, the sexual instinct and the instincts of escape and assertion.

The threatening phase is characterized by Darwin's expressive movements in pugnacity, bodily movements displayed during the activity of the instinct such as erection of hair, creation of specific noises, baring of the teeth and lashing of the tail.

McDougall points out that the instinct of combat is unrelated to the protective or parental instinct since the primary emotions of both instincts differ widely and the instinct of combat is evoked apart from connections with the offspring and also primarily concerns the male as opposed to the female.

In its extensions in man the instinct of combat is altered by intelligence and its expression is changed by social conditions and community life. These factors result in the replacement of personal aggression by collective aggression while the evolution of the sentiments and the influence of customs, religious creeds and the growth of the consciousness of the ideal self tend to obscure its manifestations and to maintain a measure of repression regarding its outward display. On the other hand, the instinct of combat supplies a source of energy which is utilized in the achievement of goals originating from the working of other instincts.

(*f*) The Instinct of Food Seeking or Nutrition.

The primary emotion accompanying the operation of this instinct is appetite, craving or gusto. McDougall regards this instinct as paramount to all other instincts and describes it as the first impulse to be distinguished from the primitive libido. It is obvious that the instinct of nutrition must be primary in the scale of human and animal instincts and that its impulse, perforce, must predominate over all other instinctive urges. Amongst living organisms the impulse to seek food by investigating and searching differentiates plants from animals. In insects the nutritious instinct is highly specialized, in mammals it is variously specialized and in the carnivora the impulse involves wandering and hunting for sustenance.

The food and drink seeking instinct is guided in its

operation by the olfactory sensibility, but amongst mammals its urge is modified by adjustment and adaptation.

(g) The Parental, Protective or Maternal Instinct.

McDougall names this instinct as the only altruistic element in nature, since in its operation it is concerned with the preservation of the species. The parental instinct takes its place with the sexual, escape and nutrition instincts as one of the most fundamental instinctive urges.

The parental instinct is remarkable for its lack of specificity which is seen in many mammals and which reaches its highest level in man in which its protective impulse is extended not only to children but to any organism in need of help. Here reason is involved as one factor of a complex whole acting as a stimulus in the same way as the whole itself. The impulse of the parental instinct is aroused by the exhibition of distress in the young rather than by the young themselves and the operation of the instinct tends to lapse when the young grow up. In its extensions the protective instinct is conditioned by similarity and contiguity and anything that is either similar to or connected with the normal instinctive object will excite the protective urge.

The primary emotions accompanying the operation of the instinct are love or tenderness and this emotion has close affiliations with the primary emotion (anger) of the combative instinct. McDougall points out that justice and law originate from moral indignation which, in turn, is based upon the two emotions of anger and love. In community life these factors are of importance since enforced acquiescence to the law can only be adequately achieved by the weight of the moral indignation of a majority within the social structure. Should this majority support fail the law can only be enforced by dictatorial powers. Again, the evolution of moral codes is dependent upon the altruistic element in the parental instinct which forms the basis of social stability, customs and family life which are fundamentally dependent upon the altruism displayed in pity and benevolence.

Hence in man the parental instincts in its ultimate extensions is modified by intelligence and reason and, while its operation may be impeded by the personal aims of the individual, the support of social sanctions augments the instinctive urge and maintains a balance between the egoistic aspirations and the altruistic aims of the instinct. Where increasing intelligence may tend to obviate altruism the social sanctions, which are a part of any religious or legal system serve as agents in the support and development of the parental instinct.

(h) The Instinct of Self-Assertion.

McDougall combines self-assertion with the self-display which is prominent in gregarious animals during the mating season. This view has received much criticism. In man, however, the instinct of self-assertion is obvious in its full operation but may be repressed or sublimated by the complex condition of community life.

Ribot described the accompanying primary emotion attached to the working of the self-assertive impulse as positive self-feeling which may be better named elation, pride or masterfulness.

The instinct of self-assertion attains its greatest intensity in man and may be regarded as a social instinct operating only in the presence of spectators who are considered inferior by the individual concerned. Because of the exigencies of community life many forms of instinctive activity must be repressed or become sublimated and self-assertion in particular suffers repression. Adler, in his individual psychology, has recognized the instinctive cravings of self-assertion under his concept of the masculine protest which is typified by the wish to dominate and the desire for superiority.

Should, however, thwarting of instinctive activity take place, unconscious inferiority results, according to Adler's view, and over-compensation may produce characteristic psychological sequelae.

Self-assertion has features in common with the instinct of self-display which is marked in the higher social and gregarious animals. The connection between self-display in animals and in man is evident in the behaviour of children and in some adults in which the present of spectators is the conditioning factor. Further, the operation of self-assertion plays an important part in the volutional control of conduct since it becomes incorporated in the sentiment of self-regard and also in the collective volition of the group or other social aggregate.

It has been stated that the primary emotion associated with the operation of the instinct of self-assertion is one of elation or masterfulness and to this must be added the appropriate derived emotion accompanying conation (striving). Shand indicated the prospective emotions of desire arising within the course of some long continued striving as the affect of confidence, hope, disappointment, anxiety, despondency and despair, all continuing within the span of conation and occurring according to the results of striving. Should the conative impulse be impeded, the despondent self evokes what shreds remain of self-assertion but despair paralyses conation and then no longer can the goal be even dimly perceived and there are only left vain regrets and the sorrowful comparison of what might have been with what is.

Here then self-assertion has lost its driving power and frustration ending in despair completes the picture. Further striving becomes useless and apathy, engendering indifference, culminates in the negation of conation. The evolution of the self and of character is retarded since volition is hindered because of the futility of further striving and the unopposed and unbalanced supremacy of the instinct of self-submission becomes evident.

The instinct of assertion is also involved in the operation of the sexual instinct. Assertion in this connection may become sadism, complicating the working of the sexual impulse and displaying itself in the psychopathology of perversion. The sublimation of sadistic trends may be observed in the dictation of the powerful and in the projection of theoretical tenets and dogmatic theories upon the masses. That the infliction of pain must inevitably occur is justified by the supposed good that the dictates might produce.

The relative intrinsic strength of the assertive impulse in individuals varies as in other instincts. The powers of adequate sublimation are important factors in the community setting. Sublimation is aided by organized knowledge, by self-reliance, by the faculty of informed criticism and, above all, by the powers of continued striving.

When the ego instincts suffer repressive forces that are inherent in the conditions of life and when the output of the energy which should flow into the assertive instinct is impeded and frustrated by the social environment, the working of the self-assertive impulse becomes overwhelmed by the opposing tendency of self-submission. This process culminates in the obliteration of self-assertion and results in the taking up of a servile and dependent mental attitude with ensuing lack of confidence and a timorous approach to reality coupled with an exaggerated respect for and ultimate fear of the causative external factors. In this situation initiative is stillborn, personal effort yields no results and collective enterprise lacks the assertive stimulus.

This state can only be combated by the powers of belief since belief alone makes action with a view to an end possible. Hence, for the persistence of conation and for the continuance of the self-assertive trends belief is a supporting and stimulating factor. It therefore follows that Descartes' dictum *cognito ergo sum* is only partially true, for to think is not the essence of existence, the added factors of effort and assertion against resistance are of fundamental importance not only in the creation of belief but also as predominating impulses in human mentality.

(*i*) The Instinct of Curiosity.

The instinct of curiosity with its primary emotion of wonder or curiosity has as its goal a fuller apprehension or a clearer percept of some object which has already evoked the operation of some other instinct. The operation of curiosity often alternates with the working of the instinct of self-preservation resulting in a mental attitude of curiosity and fearfulness. The difference between the objects or situations that excite these two instincts is a difference of degree dependent upon the amount of strangeness involved.

It will therefore be noted that the operation of the instinct of curiosity is an introductory factor towards the stimulation of some other form of instinctive response.

Curiosity operates in the two phases of approach and examination which culminate in perception sufficiently adequate to call into play other instinctive activities with a view to the taking of appropriate action. The operation of curiosity is suspended judgment resulting in discrimination and the influence of the instinct is seen in all inquiry, reflection, speculation and intellectual effort.

With the exception of the herd instinct the remaining seven instincts described above are generally accepted by most schools of psychology since they fulfil the four criteria of instinctive activity postulated by Lloyd Morgan. In other words, the resultant behaviour is innate and is not learnt by experience, while the same propensities are common to all members of the same species and are necessary to their biological welfare.

McDougall, however, describes fourteen instinctive propensities and while his views on instinctive behaviour have received much criticism, it should be noted that McDougall is more concerned with the estimation of human instinctive activity than with the instinctive behaviour displayed in animals. For this reason a brief account is given of his further classifications of instinct.

(j) The Instinct of Submission.

The operation of the instinct of submission is accompanied by the feelings of humility, subjection, inferiority and self-abasement. These negative self feelings may be experienced physically by an attitude of self-abasement, shrinking behaviour, loss of muscle tone and retarded movements. Feelings of shame and bashfulness are prominent. This emotional state originated in the primary emotion of inferiority and is designed to placate the spectator and to express submissiveness. Since the derived emotions may be regarded as blended emotions resulting from a blending of the primary emotions when two instinctive impulses are excited simultaneously, should the instinct of submission be in operation together with the instinct of curiosity, the two associated primary emotions of humility and wonder become a blended or derived emotion of admiration and again where admiration is blended with fear the secondary emotion of awe arises.

Hence, if the instinct of submission is inadequately counterbalanced by the operation of the opposed instinct of assertion and if there is concomitant excitation of the instinct of curiosity, the resulting emotional state becomes one of admiration, esteem, veneration or love of the circumstances and factors which have evoked the instinct of self-submission.

Within the community setting these factors are of considerable importance and the social implications of submission involve far-reaching consequences since, in community life, submission motivates suggestibility and the impulse of submission working in situations in which an atmosphere of power prevails produces a suggestible state of mind in the individual who becomes a ready subject of prestige and mass suggestion which, in turn, results in a mental state of submissive acquiescence to the circumstances prevailing and which welcomes the display of power and supremacy that are causal factors in evoking the submissive propensity.

The operation of the instincts of submission and assertion complicate the impulse of the sexual instinct and psychopathologically masochistic and sadistic trends are evident. Here the vital force is generated from perhaps the strongest of all instincts and the masochistic and sadistic mental content may colour mental processes apart from sexuality while at the same time drawing upon the great reservoir of the sexual impulse.

Masochistic impulses are sublimated in the community in advocacy of an opinion that is unpopular and against the desire of a majority. Great courage and intense conviction are necessary for this sublimated fulfilment but, unlike the sublimation of sadistic trends in assertion, the resulting pain is confined to the individual and is not distributed to the populus.

The practical implications of submission and assertion therefore resolve themselves from the social and community standpoints into two main factors, the psychological make-up of those individuals in power and the mentality and psychological insight possessed by those upon whom power impinges. It is clear that in community life the adequate sublimation of these two instincts are of great importance and should the self-assertive impulse be continually frustrated the unopposed action of submission will become increasingly strong, resulting in an individual and collective condition of depression with failure of interest, prominent ideas of unworthiness and of inferiority operating in a setting of pessimistic preoccupation with the futility and hopelessness of life and coloured by regretful memories of the past and anxious apprehensions of the future.

(k) The Instinct of Repulsion.

McDougall states that the instincts of fear and repulsion (repugnance) are responsible for all aversions except those acquired as the result of pain. The primary emotion accompanying the working of the instinct of repulsion is disgust, loathing or repugnance. The instinctive impulse is expressed by aversion. This instinct displays the influence of intelligence which is seen in its extensions by the process of analogy, resemblance and association. The instinctive goal is the avoidance or rejection of anything noxious and the biological value of instinct is that, aided by experience, the choice of foods becomes discriminating.

(l) The Acquisitive Instinct.

This instinct has two impulses, that of hoarding and that of garnering. Its primary emotion is the possessive feeling. In man the operation of the acquisitive instinct results in the accumulation of goods, the hoarding of capital and the creation of wealth.

(*m*) The Instinct of Appeal.

This instinct is called into play when the instinct of combat is unable to achieve its end. The goal of the instinct is to obtain aid and comfort particularly from the parents and its primary emotion is one of distress or helplessness. The cry of distress is distinctive amongst some species.

(*n*) The Instinct of Construction.

The working of this instinct is best seen in insects and birds. In man and mammals, except in the beaver, the instinct is poorly developed but in children the constructive instinct is clearly evident in such activities as play and games. In man the constructive impulse is aided by intelligence which results in co-operation in constructiveness.

(*o*) The Minor Instinct of Laughter.

Laughter, with its primary emotion of jollity, mirth or amusement, is postulated by McDougall as one of the minor instincts but this view is open to criticism on the grounds that laughter is only displayed in man and that its goal is itself. McDougall holds that laughter promotes a sense of well-being by increasing respirations and by raising the blood pressure and that its psychological function is to interrupt mental and physical activity. The operation of the instinct is stimulated by some maladjustment or something which is inappropriate in the situation or circumstances, both these factors having an attached affect of mild distress. Because of the primitive sympathetic tendency the distress which is part of the situation would be shared by the spectator who would suffer sympathetic distress. Laughter, however, prevents this sympathetic sharing and by interrupting the train of thought is an antidote to sympathy. In other words, we laugh so that we should not cry.

Other theories of laughter are those of Bergson, Hobbs and Spencer. Bergson holds that laughter operates in support of social discipline, while Hobbs postulated that laughter is the expression of pleasure. Spencer considered that laughter is conditioned by surplus nervous energy. Another view is that laughter is an attribute of the instinct of assertion and is motivated by a feeling of superiority.

CHAPTER VI

EMOTION

In elucidating emotion the same difficulty is encountered as arises in dealing with the instincts, that is, the absence of a definition of emotion which is generally acceptable. Emotion has been variously described as a variety of sensation due to general organic upheaval, as a revival of associative processes of former pains and pleasure, as a mode of conative consciousness which gives rise to the tendency towards a particular manner of behaviour or simply as a stirred-up state of mind. It is clear that because of the outward concomitants of emotional activity, emotion is not only a state of mind but also a state of the organism to which must be added the factor of consciousness. Therefore, it may be stated that emotion is a conscious stirred-up state of the organism. More detailed examination, however, is necessary before such a wide definition is adopted and a consideration of the attributes of emotion throws some light upon emotional activity.

In the first place, emotion is cognitive in so much as it signifies the nature of the impulsive reaction at work. Again, emotion is conative since there is an associated felt impulse to action. Lastly, emotion is accompanied by bodily changes which express the particular emotion in operation. McDougall emphasizes the conative factor, pointing out that should conation be removed the essential characteristic of emotion would be lost. According to this rule, where instinctive or acquired dispositions are either obstructed or facilitated, a special form of emotional experience arises. In brief, emotion is a mode or quality of experience and the varieties of emotion are the various modes of emotional experience.

Stout describes six characteristics displayed in emotion.

(*a*) The wide distribution of emotion over different stages of mental development. (*b*) The varied nature of the conditions that arouse emotion. It is rather the nature of the situation than the nature of the object that excites a specific variety of emotion. (*c*) The occurrence of a definite emotion tends to leave behind it an emotional mood akin to it. (*d*) An emotional mood, whatever may be its primary origin, tends to persist and to attach itself to any object. Hence there is a certain general trend or direction of activity involved in emotion. (*e*) The emotions are secondary to the existence of more specific tendencies which are often instinctive in nature. (*f*) In all the most intense phases of emotion organic sensations form an important constituent of the total state of consciousness.

THE JAMES-LANGE THEORY OF EMOTION

At the same time, but independently, this theory was put forward by James and Lange. The theory arises out of (*f*) above and James states his theory in these words: "My theory is that the bodily changes follow directly the perception of the exciting fact and that our feeling of the same changes as they occur is the emotion." Again, "If we fancy some strong emotion and then try to abstract from our consciousness of it all the feelings of its bodily symptoms we find we have nothing left behind." Briefly, the theory maintains that the conscious stirred-up state of mind is the complex sensation of the stirred-up state of body. In other words, emotion is not conditioned by perception but by the bodily state following on perception. As James points out: 'Without the bodily states following on the perception (perception of the external circumstances that evoke the emotion) the latter would be purely cognitive in form, pale, colourless, destitute of emotional warmth. We might see the bear and judge it best to run, receive the insult and deem it right to strike but we should not actually feel afraid or angry." James continues: ". . . the more closely I scrutinize my states the more persuaded I become that whatever moods, affectations and passions I have are, in very truth, constituted by and made up of those bodily

changes which we ordinarily call their expression or consequences; and the more it seems to me that, if I were
to become corporally anaesthetic, I should be excluded
from the life of the affections, harsh and tender alike and
drag out an existence of merely cognitive or intellectual
form."

The James-Lange theory of the emotions, therefore,
maintains that conscious emotion entirely consists of the
bodily changes that occur during an emotional experience.
These bodily changes are experienced as sensations, sensations aroused by the perception of the emotional external
stimulus. James holds that we are afraid because we
tremble, we do not tremble because we are afraid. The
emotion of fear is not experienced until the complex of
bodily sensations aroused by the external circumstances are
fully appreciated. Emotion, according to the James-Lange
theory, is simple organic sensation, a variety of sensation
due to general organic disturbance, a knowing of the bodily
state.

As has been previously indicated, McDougall emphasizes
the impulsive power of conation in emotion which displays
its working in Darwin's expression of the emotion, bodily
adaptations to the various modes of instinctive behaviour.
These "serviceable associated actions" are characteristic
and specific for each instinct. It is by the expressions of
the emotions that the operation of instinctive activity is
indicated not only in the individual but also in others.
During the experiencing of the primary emotion of fear
associated with the instinct of escape which is brought into
operation by the perception of danger, it is clear that the
danger directly arouses the required adjustments towards
the goal of escape and, as Woodworth points out, both the
preparatory bodily responses and the feeling of fear develop
after this adjustment has been elaborated. Should, however,
the end result be immediately obtained the preparatory
reactions and the feeling may not develop at all or they
may appear after the main act is accomplished. The
sequence of events, therefore, in the operation of the
instinct of escape would be (a) the perception of the

stimulus of danger, (b) recognition of the dangerous situation, (c) adjustment towards escape, (d) internal preparatory reactions and external expressive movements regarding escape, (e) conscious appreciation of the mass of sensation concomitant with these preparatory reactions, (f) definite escape reactions, (g) satisfaction and quiescence.

The following internal preparatory reactions occur in the operation of the instinct of escape. Increase in pulse and respiration rate, draining of blood from the digestive and secretory organs and its concentration in the brain, lungs and muscles, evacuation of the bladder and intestine, dilation of the pupil and the utterance of a cry of fear. According to the James-Lange theory the above organic changes comprise the emotion of fear and, in their absence, the emotion would not be experienced. It follows that should it be possible to block the appreciation of the physical changes accompanying emotional activity the conscious emotion would not eventuate. The results of physical methods of treatment in psychiatrical cases, however, would seem to emphasize the validity of the theory. From the purely psychological point of view the James-Lange theory is criticized on a number of important points. McDougall, Stout and Ladd are the principal protagonists against the theory and they base their objections upon the following points. In the first place, the results of Sherrington's experiments must receive consideration. Sherrington divided the spinal cord of a dog and hence abolished the pathway between the brain and the periphery but, in spite of the operation, when the dog was excited it exhibited the characteristic emotional reactions of anger. Stout points out that the theory lacks logic and says that while emotion and bodily alterations are conjoint it does not logically follow that they are identical. Again, should the theory be true it cannot be inverted since the organic sensation of hunger and the physical results of hyperthyroidism and such organic stimulation as the application of heat and cold—all organic sensations—do not give rise to emotion. Further, organic chances may be identical for differing emotions as in anger and fear yet dissimilar for the same emotion. In addition, the organic changes postulated in the James-Lange theory may involve the cerebrum itself and, therefore, the whole effect cannot be dependent upon sensory impulses arising from the internal organs. Stout indicates that the theory is inadequate when regard is given to emotions arising from indefinite perceptions and ideas and points out that here the primary origin of the organic sensation is a disturbance of the central nervous system. This primary disturbance being preconditioned by the organic reaction cannot be considered as its effects and is an independent factor in the constitution of the emotion. Added to these objections consideration must be given to Ladd's theory of surplus excitation, since here it is evident that the sensory impulse produces not only a special sensation in line with its specific character, but it also results in a diffuse excitement of an indefinite character which may be similar for sensations differing in their special qualities.

McDougall is of the opinion that the James-Lange theory is basically correct but he deprecates the omission of the conative aspect of emotion which is essentially the primary factor in emotional activity. McDougall suggests that the context of the theory makes mental processes too dependent upon bodily changes and would amend the theory by including the native impulse to action which, in McDougall's view, is the essence of all emotional reactions. In this connection James postulates that " I am angry because I struck," but since being angry involves an impulsive tendency to strike the proposition of " I struck because I was angry " is essentially truer since anger is conjoint with the impulse to strike. Further, McDougall points out that duplication in imagery of sensory qualities of organic sensibility is not included. Since the special senses are duplicated in imagery likewise the organic sensations may be centrally excited in the form of imagery independent of the sense organs.

To sum up in the words of Stout, it is evident that, normally, organic sensation is a contributory factor in emotion but it is by no means clear that its presence is indispensable. As Ward says, "Let James be confronted with a chained bear and then with a free bear. To the first he offers a bun, to the second a clean pair of heels.'' It is obvious that it is not so much the visual perception involved as its striking or startling character and the influence of past experience is a predominating factor.

Another aspect in the elucidation of emotional experience is offered by experiments with the psychogalvanometer (Golla). In 1888 Féré demonstrated that emotion resulted in a change in the electrical properties of the skin, lowering the resistance of the body to the passage of an electrical current. Veraguth (1904) described the psychophysical galvanic reflex and stated that it was dependent upon a secretory current associated with the sweat glands. In 1922 Golla showed that noxious stimuli resulted in a specific psychogalvanic reflex which is the expression of a diminution of skin resistance. In true emotional perturbation the screen showed the fluctuations of the psychogalvanometer, but in such psychological conditions as hysteria the psychogalvanometer failed to register.

It would appear that the psychogalvanometer gives but little support to the James-Lange theory and that while normally organic sensation is a contributory factor in the causation of emotion it does not follow that it is an indispensable condition.

CLASSIFICATION OF THE EMOTIONS

The emotions are varieties of emotional experience and are subdivided into primary, secondary and derived emotions.

The primary emotions are modes of experience which accompany the working of instinctive impulses. McDougall enumerates fourteen instincts including the minor propensity of laughter, each with its accompanying primary emotion. These primary emotions are nostalgia (herd), elation (assertion), inferiority (submission), lust (sexual), possession (hoarding), constructiveness (construction), distress (appeal), jollity (laughter), tenderness (parental), anger (aggression), wonder (curiosity), appetite (food seeking), disgust (repulsion), and fear (escape).

McDougall stresses the rôle that the emotions play in instinctive behaviour and the operation of such emotions as anger, fear and sexual desire are paramount from the biological aspect. The primary emotions arise in the operation of the instinctive impulses and since McDougall's list of instinctive propensities has been criticized on the grounds of numbers, so has his accompanying primary emotions been subjected to differing opinions. Most psychological schools, however, agree upon the presence of such primary emotions as anger, fear, lust, disgust, curiosity, tenderness and mirth accompanying the working of their appropriate instinctive drive.

The primary emotions come into operation as the results of thinking of some object or situation and they do not presuppose an impulse which is already in operation. While the primary emotions are always attached to their corresponding instinctive disposition they are essentially characterized by their conative attributes and reinforce the striving of instinctive activity by their inherent drive and purpose. An important attribute of the primary emotions is that they become organized within the sentiments which are themselves an organized system of emotional tendencies.

The secondary emotions result from a blending of the primary emotions and they arise when two instinctive impulses are excited at the same time. Here the primary emotions concerned may be blended in different proportions and in varying numbers as in the blending of the primary emotion of submission and wonder which results in the secondary emotion of admiration. Should, however, the instinctive impulses conflict with each other the attached primary emotion of one of them is inhibited as in aversion and the food-seeking instincts. On the other hand when the instinctive drives co-operate the attached primary emotions blend together as in anger, disgust and elation, which results in the secondary emotion of scorn while the blending of admiration with fear results in the secondary emotion of awe. The derived emotions are feelings as well as emotions as is shown by belief and doubt which are both derived emotions and states of feelings. The derived emotions are emotions derived from the operation of a predominating strong impulse or tendency under varying conditions. McDougall defines the derived emotions as being the results of the interplay of cognition and conation. They are the imaginative appreciation of the probability of success or failure of conation and are incidents in the operation of the instinctive impulses. They lack, however, the driving power of the primary emotions and serve to colour the working of mental processes by such affects as joy, chagrin and surprise. Hence the derived emotions are but incidents in the operation of instinctive activity and, unlike the primary emotions, do not become organized within the mental structure.

Shand, in his prospective emotions of desire was the first to draw a distinction between emotion and sentiment. He states that emotions " are in a sense adjectival and qualify a more stable feeling, whereas the specific organization of our sentiments—affection for our friends, the home sentiment and every sentiment that we can express in the term love, such as love of knowledge, art, goodness, love of comfort and all our interests, as interests in our health, fortune and profession, interest in books, collections, self-interest—these, so far from being mere adjectives and qualifying other feelings, are the relatively stable centres to which the first attach themselves, the substantives of these adjectives, the complex wholes which contain in their possible life history the entire gamut of the emotions."

While the derived emotions result from the interplay of cognition and conation, Shand has pointed out that conation alone is responsible for the prospective and retrospective emotions of desire. Confidence, hope, anxiety, despondency and despair all presuppose the operation of some strong conative impulse. These prospective emotions of desire arise in the course of any activity sustained by conation, a conation which is independent and operating prior to the rise of these emotions. The retrospective emotions of desire arise when conation is directed towards the past, and therefore regret, remorse and sorrow are sustained with conation. The psychopathological implications of Shand's work are of considerable importance.

THE FEELINGS AND THE EMOTIONS

It has been aptly stated that feeling is subjective and unanalysed. Feeling, however, is conscious but not cognitive since it tends to vanish if introspected. Feeling lies in the background of consciousness and is a conscious subjective condition. Psychologically considered, feelings are elementary, emotions are complex but emotions are agreeable or disagreeable according as to whether the conative tendencies are thwarted or gratified. Pleasure and pain are true types of feeling and are conditioned by the interplay of cognition and conation. Appreciation of conation results in pleasure and appreciation of the failure of conation is accompanied by pain.

Pleasantness and unpleasantness are simple feelings but, in reality, are complex mental states which may include sensations and thoughts with their attached affect. Feelings, however, are not sensations since they cannot be so readily analysed and introspected nor can they be definitely localized. They are inherent but have no special sense organ although feeling tone tells upon sensation to a marked degree. Feeling tone, however, is markedly individual and subjective varying with the personality and with the individual and with the individual condition at the time. There is some evidence that feeling tone is influenced by neural adjustment, pleasantness being maintained by the continuation of the normal, unpleasantness being promoted by the need for new adjustments. Neurologically, the mechanism governing such adaptation is probably located in the thalamus since the results of alteration in affect following leucotomy would seem to support such an hypothesis.

Wundt postulated a tri-dimensional theory of feeling: pleasantness and unpleasantness; tension and release of tension; excitement and quiescence. This theory, however, has not found many adherents since the basic factors of pleasantness and unpleasantness become complicated by added factors. The fact remains that conation is pleasant or unpleasant according to its results just as an emotion is agreeable or disagreeable according to the thwarting or gratifying of the conative tendencies involved.

The derived emotions are similarly conditioned. They are imaginative appreciation of the probabilities of success or failure of conation and hence the derived emotions are feelings or affections. McDougall holds the view that the derived emotions result from a differentation of the fundamental forms of feeling as typified in pleasure and pain. He assumes that this differentiation follows the organization and growth of the imagination and the increase of the capacity for hedonic tone that results from mental development.

In the integrated and developed mind all primary emotions involve conation and cognition of the degree and probability of the success or failure of conation. It therefore follows that experiences of the primary and secondary emotions are complicated by the derived emotions or feelings. They are tinged by pleasure, pain, anxiety or joy.

The emotion attached to instinctive desires and wishes is more properly from the psychopathological viewpoint described as affect. One of the most important basic problems of mental life is the disposal of affect. This emotional attachment which is primary in all mental processes and particularly in those mental activities which are concerned with the disposal of the libido and its attached emotional tone is characterized by a tendency to become displaced from its previous attachment and to seek attachments to processes entirely disconnected with the previous activity.

CHAPTER VII

THE SENTIMENTS

On the perceptual plane the actual presence of a dangerous situation excites fear; on the ideational plane the ideal prevision of a similar situation has a similar effect. As Stout points out, what is true of perceptual process holds for ideational process. Hence the general characteristics of emotion apply equally to perceptual and ideational process. On the perceptual plane, however, emotions are principally secondary and presuppose the existence of specific tendencies, particularly instinctive. On the ideational plane the specific tendencies which condition the occurrence of emotion are much more varied and complex than the primary perceptual tendencies. Each system of ideas is a general tendency to feel and act in certain ways under certain circumstances. The general name for ideal systems considered from this viewpoint is sentiment, and Stout indicates that emotions which presuppose mental dispositions organized through previous trains of ideational activity may be regarded as episodes in the life history of sentiments. A sentiment is an organized system of emotional tendencies involving an individual tendency to experience certain emotions and desires to some particular object. A sentiment is a disposition, a tendency to experience a particular type of conscious state in certain circumstances. Further, a sentiment is an acquired disposition and although originating in the innate instincts and developed from them, is elaborated and directed, to some extent, by external factors such as environmental conditions.

McDougall emphasizes the conative trend in sentiment and defines sentiment as an enduring conative attitude towards an object set up by the experience of the individual. While an instinct is a directed conative trend which is innate, a sentiment is an acquired enduring conative trend directed towards some particular object, the term object being used in its widest sense. It is important to differentiate between emotion and sentiment. The emotion is an actual state of consciousness, a mode of experience or a fact of activity. A sentiment is a complex emotional disposition manifesting itself variously under varying conditions. The varying manifestations are the actual experiences which are called emotions. Emotion is a mental function, sentiment is a mental structure with a cognitive and conative element which endure in a more or less quiescent condition between the occasions upon which it is brought into play. Emotion is the feeling tone which accompanies perception of internal or external situations, sentiment is an affective-cognitive conative association permanently laid down in the mind that determines the actual state of feeling accompanying certain perceptions. Learning by experience plays its part in the development of sentiment which, in time, becomes integrated into the mental equipment. The formation of the sentiment involves mental adaptation and adjustment, particularly in the relationship of the sentiments to community life and it is here that conflict may develop when it becomes necessary to reform a sentimental system that is at variance with the environmental conditions.

A sentiment is said to be concrete when it is attached to a definite object, for example, the sentimental attitude towards one's school or university. Generalized sentiments are concerned with abstract qualities. In this category are the aesthetic and ethical sentiments while the sentiments of regard for truth, probity and right-doing profoundly influences the intellectual reasoning processes.

The sentiments may be clasified as moral, aesthetic and intellectual. Moral sentiments are social, religious or ethical and, in general, are evolved by suggestion and observation of admired personalities and percepts. The moral sentiments are a check to the instinctive impulses and therefore a control on conduct. They are cultivated by example, education and training. The appreciation of beauty, art, music and literature is dependent upon the growth of the aesthetic sentiments and the influence of adequate educational methods during the formulative period of life is a factor of importance in their evolution. The intellectual sentiments are the foundations of belief and disbelief since where beliefs are organized into systems they become incorporated into the sentiments.

The moral and ethical sentiments are of the utmost importance in the growth of character. Honesty and dishonesty, truth and falsity, right and wrong, good and bad are abstract qualities which become organized into sentiments and the more powerful the moral and ethical sentiments the more integrated and more stable is the character. On the other hand, the more concrete and personal the sentiments are the simpler is the personality. McDougall says that the moral as well as the physical attributes of admired personalities are cultivated and, ultimately, the moral sentiments of the herd become the desired goal. The faculties of reasoning and reflection tend to extend and refine the moral sentiments and to promote moral culture. These abstract sentiments become organized and elaborated very largely as a result of example and percept during the early period of life. While the influence of education and moral teaching is of value, parental example, environmental conditions and wise choice of associates are predominating factors in the inculcation of the moral sentiments and in the growth of character. Delinquency and anti-social activities in young persons are but little influenced, after a certain age, by educational methods, but suggestion and sympathetic contagion from the observation of admired personalities are prime factors in fostering the growth of the abstract sentiment.

THE SENTIMENT OF SELF-REGARD

The sentiment of self-regard is another abstract or moral sentiment which is of paramount importance. This permanent disposition influences the personal attitude towards personal thought and personal conduct. All action and all feeling is coloured by its operation and its standards are preserved by every means possible since, should they be lowered, self-respect suffers by the impingement of limitations upon the self-regarding sentiment.

Rooted in the two conative dispositions of self-assertion and self-submission, this sentiment is the strongest and most prevalent of all sentiments. Preservation of equal balance between self-assertion and self-submission is necessary and is normally accomplished resulting in self-respect. Should, however, self-assertion predominate the ensuing sentimental trend is one of pride and psychopathologically megalomania. Where self-submission is paramount, self-abasement and humility colours the mental outlook to the detriment of self-respect.

McDougall holds that the self-regarding sentiment is universal and that the self is always regarded in conjunction with its social circumstances. The concept of the self is elaborated from the experiences of striving as the self asserts itself against other selves in the community setting. Adaptation to the social environment is necessary and reward and punishment accrues to the self according to its acts. Self-assertion and self-submission give rise to cognition of the self's capabilities and limitation. On the higher intellectual level, public opinion, moral approval and moral censure are substituted for reward and punishment and so the self learns by suggestion and persuasion to erect a system of beliefs regarding itself, to judge itself and to wish to realize in action the ideal of conduct which it has formulated and accepted.

The sentiment of self-regard becomes extended to the individual possessions and family and, ultimately, to the various social groups in which the individual has its being. The sentiment of self-regard has much influence upon morality for the erection of standards and ideals of conduct are implicit in its operation and, hence, criteria are laid down of which the self in action is cognizant, and according to the degree of self-regard wishes to achieve.

THE EVOLUTION OF CHARACTER

The character of an individual is the sum total of his innate and acquired tendencies to reaction, including those reactions that affect his life and social relations. The units of character are the sentiments and as the personality evolves the sentiments become more organized, inter-dependent and cohesive. Commonly, however, a small group of sentiments predominate and influence character formation with consequent influence upon conduct.

In the early years of life conduct is conditioned entirely by the pleasure-pain principle. Self-interest is dominant. The self-regarding sentiment which determines all conduct is but present in a rudimentary form and often does not progress beyond this infantile stage with the result that the adult continues to guide his conduct by self-interest alone and character remains undeveloped and primitive.

Normally, however, the sentiment of self-regard develops and expands and with it the growth of the altruistic and moral sentiments. Ultimately, the mental disposition be-come organized into the personality and character is slowly built up with the aid of experience and the guidance of increasing intelligence and knowledge. In the final stage knowledge becomes systematized and the growth of the sentiments expand to include all feelings, and with the in-corporation of the sentiments into the main sentiment of self-regard, social man emerges as a well-integrated and adapted organism.

Moral character is, therefore, built up by the sentiments which in their evolution are much dependent upon sugges-tion, imitation, training and education. It is clear, how-ever, that the instinctive tendencies are essentially stronger than the moral sentiments. While the moral sentiments play an important rôle in the subjugation of instinctive trends there is an unknown quality that may play the major part.

Throughout the ages philosophy has postulated many theories regarding the nature of this unknown factor. Plato believed it to be reason, Butler thought it to be conscience and James explained it as the fiat of the will. Shaftesbury considered that "good taste" was the dominating factor but perhaps one of the most reasonable of the theories extant is that of McDougall who regards it to be an impulse awakened within the sentiment of self-regard, the desire of the self to realize in conduct the ideals of conduct which the self has elaborated.

THE FORMATION OF SIMPLE SENTIMENTS

A simple sentiment is formed through the repeated evocation of some one instinctive response by some one object. It is a single conative disposition associated or linked with a single affective conative disposition.

Admiration is a true emotion, being a complex affective state in which there is inherent a degree of mental development since it is not present in animals or in young children. On analysing admiration it would appear that there are two primary emotions taking part in the production of this affective state—wonder (curiosity) and humility (submission).

McDougall shows that wonder is depicted in the impulse to approach and contemplate the admired object. Here the instinctive impulse of curiosity is in operation with its attached primary emotion. In addition to the working of the instinctive trend of curiosity there is also aroused the instinct of submission, primarily a social instinct which implies the co-operation of some person, agency or power that, being greater than the observer, is regarded with submission and humility. Hence, admiration is composed of wonder and humility, but should the admired object be of a threatening or mysterious nature the emotion of the instinct of escape—fear—will be excited. Here then admiration, which is composed of wonder and humility, becomes blended with fear resulting in the formation of the sentiment of awe. Should further blending take place and gratitude become incorporated with awe the sentiment of reverence is evolved which is basic in the evolution of all religious systems.

On considering the formation of the sentiment of reverence it is clearly evident that a sentiment is an organized system of emotional dispositions centred around the idea of some object. Factors that influence the organizations of the sentiments are determined by experience and, therefore, the sentiment is not innate but acquired.

McDougall, who expanded and elaborated Shand's concept of sentiment as an organized system of emotional tendencies, is definite upon the great importance of the concept in its relationship to character, conduct and the organization of emotional and social life.

It is of some interest that it would appear that that great sentimentalist, Lawrence Sterne, was the first to introduce the word " sentimental " to the English language, which he did in his " Sentimental Journey " published in 1768. Shand's concept of sentiment followed much later but the psychological insight of Sterne is remarkable in its accordance with modern views on the sentiments.

MOOD

Stout points out that there are two sources of emotional states, emotions arising in connection with definite perceptions or ideas and emotions that may be primarily conditioned by organic changes. Since organic sensation is diffuse there results a general change in the state of the nervous system which is reflected psychologically and experienced as an emotional mood. An emotional mood is not the same as an emotion. An emotion is felt in relation to some definite object, a mood is not related to any definite object but tends to find objects for itself. A definite emotion, however, tends to leave behind it an emotional mood akin to it.

Moods are characterized by their persisting tendency and by their liability to become attached to any object which presents itself. An emotional mood also involves a general trend of activity which expends itself according to the circumstances.

Stout here emphasizes the fact that mood is an affective conative fact of immediate experience. The subject of a mood is always aware of its presence which is displayed outwardly in attitude and behaviour.

Organic conditions which may give rise to the production of mood are diabetes, gout, indigestion and many others, but in the absence of organic causation the evolution of a mood is usually initiated from the presence of some strong emotion whose expression is frustrated. McDougall states that primarily the presence of a mood implies subconscious persistence of conation and emotion. While emotion normally subsides into a mood, reactivation of the original emotion may occur since conation is seeking satisfaction and the emotional impulse is seeking an object.

CHAPTER VIII

THE SELF

The self is the individual and the concept of the self includes "in systematic unity the life history of the individual part, present and future as it appears to himself and to others; together with all its possible or imaginary developments."(Stout). James distinguishes the "empirical ego," the self as known, from the "pure ego," the self as knower. The attributes of the empirical ego are material, (the body) social, the recognition of the self by other selves and spiritual, states of consciousness, psychic faculties and dispositions with their feelings and emotions and their spurs to activity.

The pure ego is the thinker, that which at any given moment is conscious, conscious of the "Me" the empirical self amongst many others things. Philosophical speculations upon the pure ego have postulated that behind the passing state of consciousness there is a permanent Substance or Agent. The spirit, the soul, the transcendental ego are names for this agent which James calls the thinker. McDougall points out that the empirical self is concerned with moral conduct and character.

THE EVOLUTION OF THE SELF

Mental development at the perceptual level does not distinguish the self from the physical body and the conception of the self is implicit in the material "me." It is unlikely that the infant is competent to distinguish himself from other objects. The development of visual, cutaneous, kinaesthetic and organic sensations, being subjective, differentiates the self from object exterior to the self. Soon the child, by resisting and overcoming external things, distinguishes himself from things outside himself.

As mental development progresses and trains of ideas are evolved there is a corresponding increase in the awareness of the self and the self is apprehended as a separate entity since the self of perceptual consciousness becomes ideally enlarged and the idea of the self striving and acting in the present is extended to the self's conation in the past and future. Memory is essential to the process of development and the apprehension of the self begins to include processes of conation, cognition and affection concerned not only with things present to the senses, but also with trains of ideas. Volitions, cognitions and emotions are comprehended independently of contact between the embodied self and its actual surroundings. Added to this there is memory of past trains of ideas and reference to possible future ideational activity.

From these factors the distinction between the inner and outer selves is built up and the outer self or self of perceptual process is thought of as the visible physical body, the agent of perception and motor activity, while the inner self or self of ideational process is apprehended as something situated within the body that initiates the movements and attitudes of the organism. In addition, ideally represented objects originate organic and motor sensations which appear to be experienced by an internal self.

Woodworth emphasizes the importance of resisting and overcoming external things as a prime factor in distinguishing the self from the external world and points out that it is other people more than external things that aid the self to distinguish himself and others. He makes the point that the self will realize its own entity largely from the way it differs from other selves rather than from similarity. The concept of the self is, in Woodworth's view, first appreciated by wishing, willing and striving. These factors are subjective but with increasing mental development a more objective view of the self becomes apparent by an appreciation of the limitation of the self which follows the assessment of the capabilities of the self in relation to other selves. Here the inherent desire for superiority would seem likely to colour the self's opinion of itself, but, in practice, this is not bound to be the case and most individuals will give a fairly exact estimation of themselves and their capabilities which shows that there is some inherent fidelity to fact in the mentality of most human beings. Psychopathologically, this respect for truth may be much distorted.

The rôle that self-assertion plays in the evolution of the self, presupposes that the self-assertive type of individual is conscious of the self. Woodworth holds that the self-assertive impulse precedes and that consciousness of self follows and depends upon self-assertion and that self-assertion must include the experience of failure and the necessity for submission.

On consideration of the above explanations certain prominent factors emerge of which the most important is the social factor. The social factor is of paramount importance in the evolution of the self. The self must always be considered in its social setting since the self must study other selves and its attitude towards them. The view that the self thinks other selves take of it is of outstanding utility in the elaboration of the concept of the self and it is through the organization of conative tendencies that the self is aided in recognition of its own permanent unity. The self must be adapted to its social environment and during the process of adjustment practical motives have to be considered and the relationship of the self to other selves enriches the concept of the self. As is indicated by Stout, a proper estimation and appreciation of the behaviour of other selves is rooted in the data derived from the self's own experience and, therefore, when the self constructs a representation of other selves the self must construct a representation of its own subjective experience.

It follows that the self must always be studied in its social environment since it always involves the idea of its relation to other selves. The self has to consider its attitude towards other selves and must please or placate other selves since life in a community is rendered the more easy the more harmoniously its relationships function. The working of the social factor involved includes the process of imitation with its two phases of projection and ejection. Baldwin states that the two phases of imitation is evident in the evolution of the self since, in relation to superiors the self is submissive and in relation to inferiors it is an assertive self. Stout points out that the self in relationship to enemies is a combatant self. These factors influence the ideal representation that the self takes of its self as the view that the self thinks that other selves take of it is swayed by the social factor.

CONATION AND THE SELF

The factor of conation cannot be neglected in the evolution of the self. It is only when the conative tendencies become organized into self-supporting systems that the self is able to recognize its own permanent unity.

Volition expresses the self but, fundamentally, volition is the working of the conative impulses which have their origin in the instinctive dispositions. In voluntary decisions, special conations and the termination of their striving are considered in their connection with the system of trends which are part of the concept of the self. Where tendencies conflict, voluntary action is in line with the preference of the self. Hence the self is the determining and controlling agent in volition and by the exercise of such control becomes a more stable and confirmed concept.

DELIBERATION, WILL AND CHOICE

McDougall points out that during the growth of the concept of the self there is a concurrent evolution of character. It has been stated previously that character results and grows from the organization of the sentiments. Where the sentiments are developed as cohesive and mutually supporting, character becomes stable and, to some extent, predictable. Character in action is will and will implies choice and deliberation regarding volitions. It has been seen that volition is primarily the working of the conative impulses and is an expression of the self. At times the thought of the self does not immediately decide the choice of conflicting questions and here decision is delayed so that time may be afforded for deliberation.

Hence, deliberation is a condition of hesitancy and of unstable equilibrium which is resolved and fixed by voluntary decisions which are supported and identified with the concept of the self and confirmed by the social setting, the personality make-up and, finally, by the action that follows decision and terminates painful suspense. Where conative tendencies are not firmly organized but act as isolated units, impulsive action, action that is short of full deliberation and control, follows as is seen in children and in some psychoneurotic states. Self-control is dependent upon the full evolution of the concept of the self and the development of self-consciousness. It is most efficient when ideals and principles of conduct have been erected and systematized within the self.

THE ONE SELF AND THE MANY SELVES

Stout refers to an interesting aspect regarding the self and discusses the apparent appearance under certain psychological conditions of two or more selves. Stout quotes Royce, who rightly observed, "I can question myself and wait for an answer; can reflect upon my own meaning; can admire myself, love myself, hate myself, laugh at myself; in short, do or suffer in presence of my own states and processes whatever social life has taught me to do or suffer in presence of the states and processes of others."

During the experience of conscious life it sometimes appears as if there were two or more selves striving in the same conscious individual each of which is apprehended as a relatively distinct self. With the individual consciousness there exists a great diversity of trends and states. Self-conscious reflection frequently becomes isolated on one of the special modes of experience and it is regarded as if it was a relatively distinct self. Stout aptly quotes the case of a man when sober reflecting on his mental outlook and conduct when drunk. In common parlance he says, "I was not myself," and in truth he can hardly recognize himself as the same person. Again the dream self is definitely distinguished from the waking self.

In these mental situations there is always a tendency to

refuse to recognize the self which is altered by special circumstances as one and the same with the normal self. This mechanism is also found operating when the mind is occupied by conflicting impulses when it appears that there are two persons in the same consciousness, one criticizing and antagonistic to the other. The outstanding example of this state is where there is conflict between two antagonistic groups of tendencies within the one consciousness, as may eventuate in the struggle between moral principle and temptation. Here one of the two trends is often identified with the true self and the other tendency is looked upon as being something strange and unwelcome. Dependent upon the intensity of the desire, one or other of the simulated selves takes up the attitude of reproof or judgment.

By the process of a train of ideal construction, representations of the past, present and future may be evolved in which the actual conditions and limitations are disregarded according to the desire of the present.

The mechanisms described form the genesis of day dreaming or autistic thought, a process which, within limits, is of the greatest practical value since, as Stout points out the future, unlike the past, is to some extent under individual control and realization of a future self that is unhampered by the faults, imperfections and limitations of the present self, may become one of the mind's objectives.

This normal psychological process has its abnormal variant in dissociation of the personality. The difference is one of degree and not of kind.

FIXED IDEAS

An idea that is acted upon without previous volition is said to be a fixed idea. Psychologically, consciousness is dominated by the idea and volition is unable to function. Deliberation is lacking since will, which is character in action, functions imperfectly. Here the integrity of the ego is impaired and the conative trends are weak. Psychopathologically, fixed ideas are frequently a defence mechanism resulting from conflict.

The Ego

The ego of academic psychology is a concept of the identity of the self. The idea of the self is a recombination of abstractions from many individualities and is in part dependent upon physical sensations. The concept of the ego, however, includes more than the idea of the material bodily self. As has been seen, in every individual there are many selves and the ego is a reconstruction of abstractions from these.

Essentially, the ego is subjective, it is the subject of knowledge but, when the ego is thought of, it becomes the object of knowledge. James defines the ego as a collection of cephalic adjustments to which is added a feeling of something else—thought becoming its own object. The mental attributes that distinguish one person from another are personal experiences and the mode of reaction to past experiences. The ego is a feeling comprising all the feelings of the moment together with all one's bygone feelings.

Character

Character is the sum total of acquired tendencies erected on the innate foundations of disposition and temperament. Character embraces the sentiments and the habits and is influenced by the interaction of disposition and temperament with the social and physical surroundings aided by the operation of intelligence. Therefore, character is largely evolved by the individual's own efforts.

CHAPTER IX

PERSONALITY

Psychology still lacks a comprehensive definition of personality. It has been said that personality is that quality which constitutes individuality, but, individuality, like temperament and disposition are merely synonyms for the term. Coleridge defined personality as individuality existing in itself but with a nature as a ground. Mansel stated that personality, as we can conceive it, is essentially a limitation and a relation. A better definition is that personality is that which distinguishes a person from a thing or one person from another.

Woodworth attempts an analysis of personality and points out that it is related to physique, physical appearance and muscular development. Adler's masculine protest which originates in an inferiority of bodily organs and culminates in psychological inferiority emphasizes the rôle that physique and physical structure play in the evolution of the personality. Chemique, temperament and disposition are other words that have indefinite meanings. Intelligence is obviously a factor in personality and a defective native mental endowment has much influence upon the growth of the personality. The relative weakness and strength of the instinctive tendencies are clearly of importance in the evolution of personality traits. Miller postulates the three factors of inherited structure and endowment, organic somatic variations and the psychological presentation of the organism as conjointly producing the total personality which is built up from an integrated dynamic system of forces which in its inheritance and in its own history weaves the fabric of personality. McDougall is of the opinion that disposition, temper and temperament are the three principal factors that mould the personality and this view must be considered in detail.

DISPOSITION

McDougall distinguishes disposition from temperament and character and points out that such distinctions are frequently lacking. The disposition is the sum total of the instinctive tendencies. Instinctive tendencies differ in strength in different individuals and the individual disposition is the aggregation of all the innate dispositions or instincts with their specific impulses or tendencies. Hence, individual differences of disposition are conditioned by the native differences in strength of instinctive impulses or the differences in their strength resulting from use and disuse over a period of personal development. At times one or more of the innate instinctive impulses may be lacking or one of the instinctive tendencies may be disproportionately strong. For instance, the gregarious instinct may be strongly developed and as community life is fundamentally a living in the herd, the individual with a well-developed gregarious instinct is in a much more advantageous position with resulting expansion of the personality.

As Woodworth indicates, when the minor instinct of laughter is well developed the personality is enriched by a sense of humour. Dispositions may be timid, tender, irascible and so on according to the predominance of the instinctive activities involved.

This concept is based upon the manifestation of the dominating instinctive trends and hence the disposition may vary within the scale of the number of instinctive propensities. It follows that the strength of any instinctive impulse will increase in comparison to other instinctive trends when it becomes augmented by continual use. Equalization of the instinctive tendencies is therefore important in the evolution of the stable personality, and where self-control and social sanctions fail to check instinctive activity, maladjustments will result and the personality will become unbalanced and inharmonious.

TEMPER

Temper is the expression of the mode of action of the conative impulses. Striving varies in strength and persistence and in McDougall's views corresponding variations in temper result.

McDougall, in his criticism of Shand's theory of the emotions of desire, takes the view that such states as hopefulness and anxiousness may be more properly described as peculiarities of temper rather than of disposition and advocates that in temper there are three important factors, the strength of the conative impulses, their persistence or lack of persistence and the native susceptibility of conation to the influences of pleasure and pain (affectability). It is on these lines that McDougall explains the varieties of temper as being conjunctions of different degrees of these three attributes. There are numerous variations of temper—the hopeful temper, the steadfast temper, the confident temper, the fickle temper and so on. The average is an equable temper.

TEMPERAMENT

Under the heading of temperamental factors, McDougall groups a number of innate constitutional conditions of mentality that influence mental processes. Temperament is the result of the metabolic and chemical changes that are constantly taking place in the body, and, as in the days when medicine was largely a matter of treating the "humours" or bodily fluids, and referring temperamental traits to a surplus of blood, bile, phlegm and spleen, is largely a matter of bodily constitution. In the main, natively determined, temperament may be susceptible to environmental and mental discipline. It is obvious that alterations in temperament are produced by bodily disorders influencing the nervous system and chemically modifying its processes. Amongst diseases, phthisis and diabetes will produce modifications of temperament while alcohol and other drugs will produce a breaking down of inhibitions and a temporary temperamental alteration. Progress in the study of temperament is dependent upon physiological and medical research.

Among the factors that control and modify temperament are the endocrines. Thyroxin, the internal secretion of the thyroid gland has a profound influence upon temperamental traits. Excessive secretion of thyroxin gives rise to an increase of nervous activity and a quickening of mental processes and frequently results in an excitable, agitated and restless temperament. On the other hand deficient secretion, as in myxoedema, leads to a sluggish and torpid temperament with a retardation of mental processes. The secretion of the pituitary has much influence upon bodily growth with resulting temperamental alteration while the adrenal glands, whose secretion adrenalin—"the energy hormone, the hormone of flight or fright"—is poured out during the emotional states of fear and anger and influences the bodily preparations for action, may condition an excitable temperament and has much to do with a stirred-up state of emotion. The internal secretions of the sex glands stimulate and develop the reproductive instinct and determine sexual appetite.

The organic sensations arising from the bodily organs (the coenaesthesia) colour and tone mental processes. A good digestion aids in forming a cheerful and contented temperament, a poor digestion may give rise to an irritable and peevish temperamental tone. An active muscular system favours an alert and confident habit of mind. The degree of liability to fatigue, the rapidity of recuperation, the excitability, rapidity of response and transmission of the nervous impulses are factors of nervous tissue that have a bearing on temperamental traits. Bodily peculiarities such as short stature, deformity, irregularity of features, and degree of muscular development tend to influence temperament and may lead to inferiority feelings which may be compensated by over-confidence and undue self-assertion.

PERSONALITY

It has been seen that, in McDougall's view, disposition, temper and temperament are the raw materials of personality derived from heredity. On these foundations the personality is built aided by the guidance of increasing knowledge and intelligence and fostered by experience and example.

The ultimate criterion of an individual's personality is the way that he reacts to life. Here the factors of adaptation and adjustment are crucial. The influences of environment, social conditions, education and the degree of evolution of the moral and ethical principles are of the highest importance in moulding and refining the personality particularly in the formulative years of life. The innate factors of disposition, temper and temperament may, under favourable circumstances of upbringing, family life and mental training be modified and expanded towards the necessary goal of the well-integrated personality, capable of making those inner and outer adjustments that are imperative both for the individual and for community life.

NORMAL PERSONALITY TYPES

Type psychology has extended within recent years to a degree in which all mankind may be classified and appropriately pigeon-holed. This is in line with the modern evolution of political theory that neglects the intrinsically individual and elevates the group. Standardization is necessary to bureaucracy, a system of government which, by definition, controls every detail of public and private life and psychological trends of theory have played their part in formulating and supporting political views and expedients.

Type psychology is a valuable aid to diagnosis in mental disorder, in prognosis it forms an instrument that used judiciously may anticipate future eventualities. Type psychology, with its attendant adjuvant of mental testing, however, has its limitations and while for a certain type of mind it provides an easy but often unreliable guide, it must not be overlooked that the attributes of personality are involved and only moderately static and that the only real test of individual personality is the mode of reaction to the life situation. It lies within the capacity for adaptation and adjustment to augment or hinder personality traits with their ensuing influence upon conduct and it is within the province of psychology to evolve methods of teaching and assimilating those factors which are inherent in adaptation and which, if inculcated in the developing personality, would, perhaps, to a considerable degree offset the influence of innate tendencies.

Tendencies towards a certain type of reaction have been extensively examined by psychologists over a long period of years. The correlation of a certain physical type with a certain psychological type has been postulated by Kretschmer, MacAuliffe and Sigaud. Berman sought, with but moderate success, to explain personality trends as dependent upon endocrine secretions. Kooy and Crile are other workers in this field. Eppinger and Hess differentiated vagotonia and sympatheticotonia, Kraepelin distinguished the schizophrenic and manic-depressive groups and laid the foundations for the more modern concepts of cyclothymia and schizothymia, while Stransky depicted intrapsychic ataxia as fundamental in schizothymia. Bleuler designated normal types showing cyclothymic reactions as syntonic by which is meant equally toned, attuned and harmonious. The cyclothymic approximates physically to Kretschmer's pyknic type or the so-called *type rond digestif* of the French school. Jung, in his concept of the wide type distinction between extroversion and introversion found it necessary to qualify its inadequacy by subdivision of function and postulated thought, feeling, sensation and intuition as sub-types. Here he followed the faculty school of psychology as typified by Bain who divided the mind into the cognitive, affective and volitional aspects and classified personality as intellectual, emotional and volitional. Ribot had previously grouped personality types under the sensitifs and actifs, the emotional and the energetic, the pessimists and the optimists.

While Jung's classification has been criticized upon its adherence to faculty psychology and its disregard of the essential dynamic qualities that a life situation demands, its broad outline and definite depiction of the two pre-dominant personality trends in mankind requires further detailed description.

THE SCALE OF INTROVERSION

Jung distinguishes introversion and extroversion as the

end points of a continuous scale of introversion. The introvert is characterized by that retreat from reality that psychopathologically, typifies the schizophrenic. The pathological manifestation is a matter of degree and not of personality. Moody, cold and aloof the introvert pursues his way indifferent to the demand of social life and intent upon the working out of his own mental processes. Repressed and subjective, his normal emotional tendencies are denied expression and that sympathy which McDougall postulates as inherent in emotion and social life is inhibited and neglected. Negation of impulse and emotion leads to a solitary brooding and a reflective state which is concerned with internal problems of adaptation and with the working out of the complex manifestations of efforts to achieve reality which, because of the personality viewpoint, are beyond fulfilment. This shut-in personality debars the introvert from the struggle and perturbations of community life and isolated and without the common touch he lives in a world dominated by his inhibitions and yet conscious of the loss of primitive sympathy and of that rapport with his fellow creatures which is the essence of the gregarious instinct. It must not be thought that the introvert does not contribute to the common weal. This type of personality is adapted to the elucidation of theoretical questions and, in any community, is the originator of planning and the recorder of events. Integrated in his special functions and the custodian of knowledge, the introvert plays his part in the estimation of basic principles and in those intellectual occupations which add the flavour to human existence.

The main body of human beings, while tending either towards introversion or extroversion, fall more frequently within the category of extroversion and display the syntonic or cyclothymic type of reaction. Sociable, clubable and adapted to the demands of community life, the extrovert has his interests directed towards the environment, unlike the introvert whose libido is turned inwards. In extroversion the outward direction of the libido renders mental proceses objective and hence the extrovert is continually in contact with reality and his reactions are associated with his environmental situation in contra-distinction to the introvert whose subjective outlook tends to neglect reality. Emotional and impulsive, the extrovert expresses his personality in action, speech and behaviour.

Kretschmer has correlated the pyknic (compact) type of physique with his cycloid personality type. The pyknic is characterized by a largeness and fullness of bodily build with a square head, thick neck and ample abdomen and Kretschmer's cycloid type has many points in common with Jung's extrovert as has Kretschmer's schizoid personality with introversion. Physically, Kretschmer connects the schizoid and introvert with the asthenic (lacking force) type of physique with its small head, long neck, narrow chest and long skeletal structure. Further subdivisions of this asthenic physical type are the dyplastics who show various forms of growth abnormalities and the athletics who also frequently show dysplasia. In general, the schizoid or introverted personality type is most commonly found in association with the dyplastic or astheno-athletic type of bodily build while the pyknic physique characterizes the extrovert.

Jung's conception of introvertion has points of similarity with James's tender-minded, the Apollonians of Nietzsche, the devouring of Blake and with Meyer and Hoche's "shut in" personality. Neurologically, there are some factors that connect introversion with the vagotonia of Eppinger and Hess.

In the same way Jung's extroversion has aspects of similarity with James's tough minded, Nietzsche's Dionysian and Blake's prolific. Neurologically there is a similarity to sympatheticotonia. In addition, the endocrine pattern in these two main personality types has much bearing upon their differentiation.

Clear-cut and well-defined examples of the introvert and extrovert are infrequently found and a mixture of the two types is common. The position of the individual upon this personality scale is largely dependent upon native constitution but it is susceptible to environmental, educational and disciplinary influences especially during early years of life.

CHAPTER X

REASONING, BELIEF AND DOUBT

Locke defined reason as a faculty of the mind by which it distinguishes truth from falsehood and good from evil and which enables the possessor to deduct inferences from facts or from propositions. Man is supposed to be the only rational animal and by some special faculty alone found in human beings which is called conscience, the moral sense, the rational will, the sense of duty or reason is raised above all other animals. As Stewart said, reason is used to express the whole of those powers which elevate man above the brutes and constitute his rational nature, more especially his intellectual powers.

This traditional intellectualist philosophy is, as Mc-Dougall points out, incompatible with the principle of evolution and is a form of the faculty doctrine whose fallacies have so often been exposed. The function of reason is merely to deduce new propositions from propositions already accepted. Reason only directs pre-existing tendencies towards their appropriate objects and, unless desire to achieve these objects is operating, reason cannot create desire. That is, for example, unless the moral sentiments are well established, reason alone will not impel the individual to either do good or desire to do good. That caustic philosopher Voltaire remarked that many are destined to reason wrongly; others not to reason at all; and others to persecute those who do reason.

James distinguishes rational thought from reasoned thought and indicates that most of our thinking consists of trains of ideas suggested one by another and linked by contiguity or similarity. This type of thinking is irresponsible thinking concerned with empirical concretes not with abstractions. In reasoning, although results may be thought of as concrete things they are not suggested, as in simple associative thinking, by other concrete things but are linked to the concretes which precede them by intermediate steps which are formed by abstract general characters articulately denoted and expressly analysed. Hence a thing inferred by reasoning need not be either habitually associated or similar to the datum from which it is inferred and, in fact, may be a thing entirely unknown to our previous experience, something which no simple association of concretes could ever have provoked.

The essential difference between rational thinking and reasoning lies in the fact that empirical thinking is only reproductive and reasoning is productive. Reasoning is the process by which unprecedented situations are understood and it is by making inferences from unfamiliar data that new concepts are evolved. Hence reasoning is the ability to deal with novel data by analysis and abstraction. James, therefore, defines reasoning as the substitution of parts and their implications or consequences for wholes. Further, the reasoning process comprises sagacity, the ability to discover what part—the essential attribute—lies in the whole before consciousness, and learning, or the ability to promptly recall the implications, consequences and concomitants of the essential attribute. The abstraction of the essential attribute from the concrete datum, in logic, the minor premise or subsumption, requires the sagacity, the major premise, the essential attribute and the attributed property requires learning. James points out that usually learning is more apt to be ready than sagacity, the ability to discriminate fresh aspects being rarer than the ability to learn old rules and, therefore, in most cases of reasoning the minor premise or the way of conceiving the subject is the one that makes the novel intellectual achievement. James cogently says that emphasis and selection seem to be the essence of the human mind. The essence of a thing lies in the fact that one of its properties is of such importance for the present interest that in comparison with it the rest of its properties are neglected.

Reasoning always operates to attain some particular

conclusion or to gratify some special curiosity. Reasoning analyses the datum, conceives it abstractly and conceives it rightly according to that particular abstract character which guides the reasoning process to the conclusions which are the reasoner's temporary interest to attain. To sum up, James postulates two major points in reasoning. In the first place, an extracted character is taken as equivalent to the whole datum from which it originates. In the second place, the character thus taken suggests a certain consequence more obviously than it was suggested from the total data. In brief, in the words of Garbett, the prerogative of reason is to remember the past, to anticipate the future and to realize the absent.

Woodworth, perhaps superficially, refers to the reasoner as an explorer whose explorations may result in the perception of some fact previously unknown to him. On these lines reasoning is described as mental exploration, first by the method of trial and error and then by the use of mental processes. On the question as to whether man is the only reasoning animal it is pointed out that the behaviour of animals is impulsive and governed by motor responses. It appears to be clear that the animal does not recall facts previously observed nor does it adduce their bearing upon any particular problem. The point emphasized is that the animal works by motor explorations whereas man uses his mental equipment.

Animal behaviour, however, differs from human behaviour in the study of problems, in the effort to recall relevant facts which may influence a solution and in the accumulation of past experience. Woodworth calls reasoning a trial and error process in the sphere of mental reactions but in human beings the accumulated knowledge of the past, aided by the predominating mental interest in the present problem results in the operation of intelligence and acquired learning which are principal factors in human mentality. Perception by inference in reasoning, however, is particular to mankind and while the result is an inferred fact its application may culminate in a general rule and the inference then is concerned with the application of the general principle to the special case. Here indirect comparison predominates. A false inference is a fallacy which commonly results from neglect to appreciate the true relationship between the facts presented.

While reasoning according to this view is inference resulting from mental exploration, the nature of the exploratory purpose varies according to the situation, the motives at work and the sequence of events. Here recall of of past events influences inference.

In seeking for an explanation, which is a comparatively simple form of reasoning, the present interest is objective rather than subjective. The instinct of curiosity is aroused and previous knowledge is called upon and a deduction is made from an accepted general principle. Man's reasoning processes commonly originate from the application of the general rule to the particular circumstances. Here motivation is application of the general to the particular and the necessary inferences are drawn which not only make their general application more obvious but throw light upon the particular instance involved.

BELIEF

Stout states that the clearest of the cognitive attitudes is that of belief with which stands in contrast the attitude of supposal. The characteristic of supposal is that the mind has a range of arbitrary choice between alternative suppositions. It is characteristic of belief that the alternative believed in is determined for the mind and not by it, being imposed on the mind by the nature of the object with which the mind is concerned. Here doubting and questioning belongs to the attitude of belief rather than to that of supposal. Doubt is distinctive in so far as doubting implies the freedom to make alternative suppositions. Stout emphasizes that this freedom is felt as an obstacle which must be overcome because the mind is in a state of suspense and the passing of judgment is imperative. On the ideational plane the primary and pervading attitude of mind is supposal. Supposal arises when belief is not challenged. Should belief be called into play the alternatives of belief or doubt must arise. Stout points out that in mental development supposal originates later than belief. This is seen in the pretending of children and in the playful behaviour of animals.

A distinction is drawn between the free play of imagination where judgment and belief is subordinate and the conditions of belief. In imagination, any ideal combination may be possible although the play of ideal construction is restricted and subject to the confines of contradiction, but the restriction is dependent upon the general direction of mental activity at the time when the mental attitude is one of belief; the flow of ideas being restricted by the nature of the object.

Objective restriction, however, is seen in its full capacity in the pursuit of knowledge. Stout emphasizes that it is only in these cases that full belief is demonstrated—belief not blended with imagination but contrasted with it. It is likely that the attitude of belief and disbelief is prior to the free play of imagination.

BELIEF AND ACTIVITY

Bain indicated that the relationship of belief to activity is expressed in the words, "what we believe we can act on," hence practical and theoretical needs play an essential part in conditioning belief and disbelief. But belief is, at the same time, dependent on activity and on limitation of activity being, on the one hand, subservient to subjective tendencies and, on the other hand, to practical conditions. Stout aptly states that we can no more attain our ends without submitting ourselves to control independent of our wish than we can walk independently of the resistance of the ground on which we tread.

DEDUCTIVE AND INDUCTIVE REASONING

Deductive reasoning is the process whereby a general proposition is applied to special cases as in mathematics.

Inductive reasoning presupposes the need for the explanation of particular facts on the lines of a general law or hypothesis which is applicable to the given data. The general law, having been formulated, it becomes necessary to incorporate the particular facts within it. If this can be accomplished the facts must be true and the hypothesis is verified for the moment.

LOGIC AND PSYCHOLOGY

While the function of logic is to logically correct the results and validity of reasoning processes psychology is concerned with the mental processes inherent in the function of reasoning. Logic only considers the legitimate inferences while psychology is more speculative and continually active in seeking to explain the activities of the mind.

The logical inference is obtained by arriving at a conclusion from two given facts or premises which acting conjointly, arouse the perceptive response of inference. The conclusion of the logical syllogism results from the correct inference. The syllogism consists of three terms and in the example, all birds fly, the crow is a bird therefore the crow flies, the three terms are "crow," "fly" and "bird." These terms are denoted by the letters S, P and M, S being the subject concerning which an inference is drawn, P the predicate or what is inferred regarding S, and M the middle term or point of reference. When the relationship between the terms is logically correct the inference is valid. The syllogism is symbolically stated as major premises, M is P, minor premises S is M, conclusions are therefore S is P.

Woodworth follows Stout in enumerating the requisite conditions for successful reasoning, pointing out that a good variety of major premises is required which should accrue from previous experience, knowledge and memory. The minor premise results from the particular observation of the significant fact concerning the logical problem. The conclusions that are implicated in the premises are obtained by unitary response to the combination of premises which make up the percept of inference.

BELIEF, DOUBT AND JUDGMENT

McDougall, deducts his conception of belief and doubt from his view of the nature and condition of confidence and suggests that belief is essentially the same emotional state as confidence and belongs to the continuous series of the derived emotions of desire. In this view it is pointed out that action or readiness to act upon belief is the most prominent evidence available of the reality of belief. McDougall lays stress on the part played by conation in belief pointing out that belief is always determined by conation and that there is no belief without desire. The essential difference between confidence and belief is that confidence qualifies active striving towards a desired end while belief is the feeling which qualifies processes on the plane of intellectual activity which cannot issue into action at once. Doubt in this view bears the same relation to belief that anxiety bears to confidence. Doubt is anxiety on the plane of intellectual activity when action is postponed or suspended. Belief aided by memory and intelligence is evolved out of confidence and belief in its fullest sense must be preceded by doubt which is followed by judgment. Just as belief and doubt are conditioned by the interplay of conation and cognition so is judgment. Implicit judgment accompanies all cognitive processes and when affirmation or denial follows judgment, belief becomes explicit. Without interest, however, the necessity for judgment does not eventuate. In judgment there is a strong conative factor which is made apparent by the action of suggestion which may call into play the submissive impulse whose action may influence judgment, usually towards the positive aspect.

In the process of forming a judgment an abstraction is made from any percept, idea or concept and the abstraction recombined or associated with the primary percept or concept. Hence a judgment placed into words is a proposition and by reasoning a series of judgments may be made since, in this context, reasoning is verbally a series of propositions which are related to each other, the last term of the series being drawn from the preceding judgments or propositions. The conclusion may be right or wrong and it is the function of logic to indicate as to whether the inferences are legitimate.

McDougall points out that doubt may be altered to belief

by one of three cognitive methods, by definite perception, by communication from another person and by reasoning from previously established beliefs.

In intuition the individual is guided in the establishment of beliefs by feeling. Intuition is implicit apperception and is conditioned by some subtle conjunction of sense impressions that cannot be analysed, which determines the conative-emotional reaction.

Persuasion is reasoning aided by suggestion. Here there is implicit belief in what is read or heard and personal communications are accepted without full judgment being passed.

THE FORMATION OF BELIEFS

Belief and doubt are intellectual sentiments conditioned by cognition and conation and involving memory. The more active the conative factor is the more intense is belief or doubt. The conative impulse to pursue an end is also an impulse to form beliefs since ends can only be realized by the use of means and the subject has to have some belief in the efficiency of the means in order to use them.

The social factor is of importance in the formation of beliefs since individual beliefs are largely determined by the beliefs commonly held in the social strata in which the individual has his being. Again, beliefs must conform to the nature of the world in which the individual lives. Hence this objective factor is conditioned by the actual facts of existence.

True belief is belief which is not mingled with imagination and is only found in the pursuit of practical ends since here only certain combination of ideas are possible.

Belief in the reality of the self is, according to McDougall, aroused by the power of conation—of the self-striving and persisting towards a goal. Personal reality depends on effort and where the urge to exercise effort is lost a condition of depersonalization arises and the individual has the appreciation of being altered in some way and may regard himself in a new and abnormal light. Belief in the reality of others things is determined by a projection of personal reality since striving is against resistance and what exists has force and is therefore real.

The erection of systems of beliefs are carried out by reasoning, the method of trial and error taking place on the plane of imagination. Beliefs are enduring facts of mental structure which may be isolated, loosely knit or organized into systems. While most minds have detached systems of belief logically independent and without mutual support the well-integrated mind has organized supporting systems of beliefs which are coherent and consistent and logically interrelated.

The common structure of systems of belief in mankind may be compared with the crenellations of a fortress, the mind being the fortress and the indented battlements being the semi-organized yet partially disconnected beliefs. Largely isolated and mostly self-supporting, they interrupt the solid structure of the fortress of the mind by gaps in the parapet of the fortress, clefts which render the organization and integration of a comprehensive system of beliefs impossible. Hence, one belief only partially supports another while many beliefs are isolated structures within the mind without intellectual connection or logical unity. It is only when the clefts are filled in with the intrinsic supporting material that the mind may be said to function in complete unity. It is on the lines of this hypothesis that individual systems of belief require organization if the rational mind is to be achieved.

CHAPTER XI

MEMORY

Aristotle said that memory is the scribe of the soul and it is in line with this pertinent observation that James defines memory as the knowledge of an event or fact of which we have not been thinking with the additional consciousness that we thought or experienced it before. Hence memory is the custodian of the collected treasures of life, the conservative propensity, the friend of wit but the treacherous ally of invention.

James repudiates the assumption that memory is simply a revival in the mind of an image or copy of the original event and points out that such a revival is merely a duplicate that has no connection with the primary event except that it happens to resemble it. No memory is involved in the mere fact of occurrence and a further condition is required before the present image can be taken for a past original. This condition is that the fact imagined must be expressly referred to the past and thought of as in the past. But since, in time perception, intuition or immediate consciousness only gives a few short moments of pastness and it becomes necessary to conceive, not perceive more remote times, the time becomes associated with concrete events or with names or other symbols which must be thought of in order to think of the past. Hence, to revive the past it must be thought of in association with contiguous associations and, in addition, it must be dated in the personal past. It is well put by James that not only must the revived material be referred to a personal past but it must also have that warmth and intimacy which characterizes all personal experiences. Additional factors in memory are retention of the remembered facts, their recall, recollection and reproduction.

Recall was explained by Mill as recollection by association and James characterizes the machinery of association as the law of habit which also explains retention. According to this view a good memory is dependent on the number and persistence of the neural pathways. It is said of Johnson that he never forgot anything that he had seen, heard or read and the like attaches to the memories of Burke, Clarendon, Gibbon and Locke and many other eminent personalities. James postulates that the persistence and permanence of the nervous pathways involved in neural habit is a physiological property of the individual while their number is due to the facts of his mental experience. This physiological retentiveness varies very considerably from infancy to senility and from one person to another. Colton pointed out that of all the attributes of mind, memory is the first that flourishes and the first that dies.

Stout defines memory as ideal revival so far as ideal revival is merely reproduction and he states that memory is analogous to the formation of habits of thinking and acting since, as in the formation of habit, retentiveness and conation are involved. True memory consists of a reinstatement of past experiences, the experiences being reinstated in the same order and manner as in their original happening. No inferences must be drawn. In this view, remembering is a conative activity and, hence, the stronger the motive for remembering the more efficient is the recollection. An intention to remember favours remembering. Should recollection fail momentarily and then the forgotten experience emerge into consciousness, conation has been working subconsciously. Conation also influences forgetting, as is shown in functional amnesia, where the motive which prevents recollection must be overcome. This may be done by hypnosis by which the conative activities may be controlled.

McDougall postulates three factors in memory, memorizing, or the power to connect a memory, retention, retaining the traces which facilitate reproduction, and reproduction the capacity for reproducing by the aid of retention.

As has been stated above James holds that retention is due to actual persistence of brain traces. Stout maintains that the power of retentiveness is born as an essential part of the individual's physiological constitution. The factors of retentiveness and conation are also seen in habit and has led to the belief that memory and habit are identical functions. Freud holds that all experiences may be recalled since they leave a trace on the mind and that, when forgetting occurs, it is reproduction and retention that is at fault. Bergson is of the opinion that memory is not conditioned by brain traces but is a purely spiritual or mental function. He distinguishes between habit and true memory and states that memory is of the mind and habit is of the body.

Habit may depend to a large extent upon physiological pathways in the central nervous system which are formed and rendered more permanent by the passage of each nervous impulse, but this is not true of memory. It is pointed out that the past survives in motor associations and in independent recollections and, while learning by heart has all the marks of habit, the memory of each successive reading during the process of learning by heart has none of the marks of habit. In the first instance, habit is interpreted by memory, in the second case, pure memory alone is involved.

A motor habit is a secondary automatic process involving no remembering of the experience through which it was acquired. The motor habit is accumulative effect of all the successive readings and bears no unique relationship to any one of them like pure memory does. McDougall agrees with this view and states that memory is not the same as habit. He points out that a motor habit is formed by neural associations and by conation which is association by habit. True memory involves mental association or association by meaning.

Motor or habit learning is contrasted with true or ideational learning. In animals, learning is largely habit learning aided by adaptive behaviour while animal memory may be associative revival and not recall.

FACTORS IN GOOD MEMORY

Interest provides rapidity and accuracy of actual revival and also the rapidity with which the power of recalling is acquired. Interest and frequency condition the length of time the power of remembering continues. The formation of the right kind of associations influence the readiness with which memory reproduces what is relevant to the prevailing interest of the moment. A memory may be extensive and yet not serviceable. This is sometimes seen in cramming for examinations where although the candidate may know the subject matter his knowledge is unorganized and the relevent points cannot be recalled because adequate associations have not been made. As Stout remarks, to have a good memory is to have a well-organized mind.

The power of acquiring a good memory is dependent on various factors of which interest and congenital constitution are the most important. As Woodworth indicates, the will to learn must be present, and interest, confidence and visible accomplishment must be cultivated. The task must be studied as a whole and the facts and their relationships, their resemblances and contrasts must be noted. Indirect attachments should be formed and the cardinal points of the subject should be extracted with special reference to meaning, outline and broad relationships. Recency is an important factor in remembering but does not replace systematic study. Difficulty in recall depends upon the emotional state at the time, lack of interest in the past experience and doubt which is anxiety on the intellectual plane. In difficulty in recall, should the question be left for the time, frequently conation continues subconsciously and the answer may be suddenly recollected. In study and memorizing, recitation, the student reciting to himself is of much value. Recitation fixes the subject matter of study more permanently and the satisfaction of achievement is a spur to conation. Spaced repetitions are more effective than unspaced and fairly long periods of study yield better and more durable results than many periods of short study. On the question as to whether the memory can be improved by practice, James maintains that "all improvements of memory consist in the improvement of one's habitual method of recording facts." It is the power of learning not the power of retaining that is increased by practice as in actors who, studying many parts, improve their power of studying their part systematically but not their power of retention.

THE CAUSE OF FORGETTING

The rate of forgetting is at first rapid and then gradually declines and, after a time, becomes very slow. Memory traces are retained for years. Woodworth points out that more is lost in the first hour than in the second hour and more in the first week than in the second week. After two to four months experiments have shown that much is lost but that traces still remain. In the curve of forgetting the base line is the level of complete forgetfulness marked off in hours. The vertical line is graded corresponding to the number of readings made of a row of nonsense words. It may require twenty readings to learn a row. To relearn the row after five hours may require ten readings, after ten hours fifteen readings. The decay of memory increases with the lapse of time but relatively the smaller the longer the interval.

TESTIMONY

Much experimental work has been carried out with a view to measuring the reliability of the testimony of eye witnesses. In general, the results of such experiments indicate that testimony is most unreliable except for facts that were specifically noted at the time and, for these special facts, those that are in line with the observer's interests or that may have stimulated some instinctive propensity have particularly been given attention to and remembered. Happenings and objects that do not appeal to the present interests are neglected, overlooked and lack memory value.

The memory for many facts that have taken place in the presence of the witness may be most indefinite, completely lost or entirely false. Where, however, facts have a personal interest to the observer their memory is unimpaired and recollection is good. In one experiment in recall the percentages of error in answering questions were fourteen per cent immediately, eighteen per cent after five days, twenty per cent after fifteen days and twenty-two per cent after forty-five days. The percentage of error in this test was smaller than could be expected in legal testimony.

A further factor in testimony is retrospective distortion, a filling up of memory gaps by fabrications or false memories. As Burt points out, the tendency in recapitulation is for the incidents to be more concrete and more dramatic than in the original. The creation of false memories may also be accelerated by suggestion and, as a principal factor in suggestion is prestige, the testimony of witnesses in court tends to be influenced by the personality of the questioner. In this connection the psychology of rumour is of interest. Rumour, as Shakespeare writes, "stuffing the ears of men with false reports," obtains its impetus from the emotional tendency to believe what we want to believe and the more detailed and dramatic the rumour is the more its spread "increasing as rapid as the snowflake and gathering accessions every instant until it becomes an avalanche carrying destruction wherever it falls." It is in situations charged with emotional tension that rumour invariably has its genesis and here McDougall's primitive passive sympathy, the sympathetic induction of emotion in others and particularly within the herd, is a factor in spread.

CHAPTER XII

ACTION

Action is the end of all thought and is at once the destiny and the lot of man. Desire, wish, and will are states of the mind and, as James points out, no definition can make them plainer. The only direct outward effects of will are voluntary bodily movements. While reflex, instinctive and emotional movements are primary, voluntary movements are secondary functions, learnt in the first instance by experience, experience which leaves behind it an image of itself and which, having once occurred, can be an object of volition and deliberately willed. The neuro-muscular processes at work are mechanical agencies by which the voluntary movement is executed and the explanation of their operation and mechanism lies within the province of physiology. Psychologically considered, there may be two factors that intervene between the eventuation of voluntary movement and origination, these are what James calls the bare idea of the movements' sensible effects and some decision, consent or volitional mandate which is an attribute of consciousness. At times the first factor is sufficient but usually only sufficient for the fundamental and simple types of movement. This type of movement is termed ideomotor action which occurs unhesitatingly and immediately following the idea of the movement. Lotze points out that all the acts of daily life are performed in this wise and do not demand a distinct impulse of the will. The express fiat of the will or act of mental consent only arises when antagonistic or inhibitory ideas are involved. Here deliberate action arises and decision becomes necessary. The decision is the fiat of the will and is brought about by the reasons or motives which influence decision.

A further factor in voluntary action is the pleasure and

pain which the action may involve. This affect modifies and regulates voluntary action but is not the only spur to action.

In involuntary action, which operates without intention, is included reflex action, impulsive action and habit, all actions that have not been imagined before their occurrence and which usually take place without conscious impulse.

FACTORS INFLUENCING VOLUNTARY ACTION

Perhaps of all spurs to endeavour, purpose is the greatest. It has been said that purposes, like eggs, unless they be hatched into action will run into decay, but where striving is directed by definite purpose and the goal is within reach the conative impulse will automatically persist with a resulting release of energy and an increase in effort. Purpose is stimulated by achievement and visible progress which clarifies the anticipated end and supplies encouragement and increased endeavour. Another factor in the determining of voluntary effort is that supplied by the instinctive impulse of self-assertion. It is here that competition shows its stimulating value in spite of what is said regarding the evils of competition, which matter, however, is one of degree and not of principle. The acceptance, indeed, the welcoming of responsibility is an additional factor which influences voluntary action. Those constituents which make up the mental state of morale, such as hopeful expectation, zeal, confidence and belief and which, psychologically considered, are influenced by the prevailing opinion within the herd, sustain continued striving, particularly in difficult circumstances. Visible achievement supports morale, whereas frustration impedes its maintenance. Initiative, which basically is the power of commencing action, is a personality or character trait which is capable of development under favourable conditions but which becomes stillborn under repeated frustration, is a major factor in instituting voluntary action.

Where voluntary action is confronted with personal conflicting tendencies the conflict is resolved by an appeal to the self, the ideally constructed whole which comprises the ego. The ultimate arbiter in voluntary action is the concept of the self, the self knowing and striving, accepting and rejecting, experiencing and learning.

In involuntary action there is usually a defect in self-control. The strength of an isolated impulse may prevent the calling into play of the concept of the self or the degree of development of self-consciousness may be inadequate. In other cases, pathological conditions may disrupt the self leading to the carrying out of involuntary acts which are at variance with the normal personality.

AUTOMATIC ACTION

Automatic action is action that formerly was voluntary but because of constant repetition and because of the effect of training and education has become organized and, therefore, scarcely affects consciousness. Automatic action is slower than reflex action and about as quick as a simple reaction.

Automatic action is involuntary, mechanical and automatic, that is, action that takes place without being imagined before and without conscious impulse. In automatic action, attention and impulse have deserted the fully mastered details and attached themselves to larger units. Examples of automatic actions are piano playing and signing one's name.

IMPULSIVE ACTION

Impulsive action is distinguished from voluntary action by the fact that impulsive action follows the isolated conative tendency, whereas in voluntary action special conations and their goals are first considered in their relation to the total system of tendencies included in the concept of the self. Impulsive action is action short of full deliberation and control and usually occurs in organisms in which inhibition is markedly lacking as in children and animals.

Impulse is defined by Stout as any conative tendency so far as it operates by its own isolated intensity apart from its relation to a central system of motives.

HABIT

Habit is voluntary action which, from repetition and facilitation, is almost automatic. Habitual action is action to which no persistent or discriminating attention is paid to the details of the action in question. The habit is conscious but the conscious actions of habit have become stereotyped.

An acquired habit from the physiological viewpoint is a new pathway of discharge by which certain incoming impulses ever after tend to escape. James postulates plasticity of nervous tissue as giving rise to formation of habits in human beings. By plasticity is meant a structure weak enough to yield to an influence but strong enough not to yield all at once. Each relatively stable phase in such a structure is marked by what may be called a new set of habits. The plasticity of neural tissue is such that the pathways of the discharge of incoming impulses become deepened or new pathways are formed.

Habit is necessary to the organism because it simplifies and makes movements more accurate and diminishes fatigue. Whereas the performances of animals are automatic, in man, because of the great number of performances displayed, habit must be the result of learning and James points out that if practice did not make perfect nor habit economize the expense of nervous and muscular energy the number of performances would necessarily be most drastically curtailed.

Again, when action becomes habitual, each new muscular contraction is originated in its appointed order by the sensation occasioned by the muscular contraction just finished and not by a thought or by a perception. While voluntary action requires guiding by idea, perception and volition, habitual action is guided by sensation, thus leaving the higher centres comparatively free. Hence, conscious attention is much less necessary in habitual action than in voluntary action.

THE IMPORTANCE OF HABIT

It has been said that habit has so vast a prevalence over

the human mind that there is scarcely anything too strange
and too strong to be asserted of it. James refers to habit as
the enormous flywheel of society, its most precious conservative agent. Brougham, commenting on the effects of
habit, wrote: "I trust everything to habit, upon which in
all ages the lawgiver as well as the schoolmaster has mainly
placed his reliance; habit which makes everything easy and
casts all difficulties upon a deviation from a wanted course.
Give a child the habit of sacredly regarding truth; of care-
fully respecting the property of others; of scrupulously
abstaining from all acts of improvidence which involve him
in distress and he will just as likely think of rushing into
an element in which he cannot breathe, as of lying or
cheating or stealing."

The Formation of Habits

It is in the period of age below twenty that most personal
habits are formed, those habits that differentiate individuals and which confirm or betray the results of upbringing, parental example, education, training and social
milieu. The modes of vocalization, pronunciation and
address, those indefinite but strong characteristics which
distinguish the various social strata, those differences between persons that, unimportant in themselves, are inculcated in the impressionable years of youth and which cannot
be altered in maturity.

The period between twenty and thirty is the critical time
for the formation of intellectual and professional habits.
The mode and direction of thought, the evolution of preju-
dice, the growth of mannerisms, in short, the form which the
integrated personality ultimately assumes is evolved during
this formulative period. Here James uses an apt and
illuminating simile which throws much light upon habit
when he states that once the habits of mind are formed,
the man can no more escape from them than can his coat
sleeve suddenly fall into a new set of folds. By the age of
thirty the character has set like plaster and will never soften
again. It has cogently been remarked that habit makes
no figure during the vivacity of youth; in middle age it

gains ground; and in old age governs without control.

In the formation of habit the following factors are of importance. In the first place it is essential to make habitual as early as possible as many useful actions as possible and to take steps to guard against the formation of disadvantageous habits. By this process the daily details of life become automatic and the mind is set free to deal with its cognitive and conative work. In the formation of new habits and in the casting-off of detrimental habits the first principle to observe is to use a strong and decided initiative. Resolution requires support and achievement which gives momentum and any factor which will reinforce the desired habit alteration and stimulate the growth of new habits must be assiduously cultivated.

Secondly, no exception should be allowed under any circumstances until the habit is firmly rooted. Bain points out that continuity of training is the great means of making the nervous system act infallibly right. In this connection the renunciation of such habits as alcoholism and drug taking requires special consideration. From the purely psychological viewpoint abrupt termination is the better course to adopt since desire will die the sooner from inanition if it is never fed.

Thirdly, the formation of new habits is much influenced by action and the first opportunity to act on a new resolution must be taken since it is not at the moment of forming a habit, but at the moment of the habit producing its motor effects that aspirations and resolves communicate to the neural pathways the new direction. As James indicates, with mere good intentions, hell is proverbially paved. Character, in Mill's words is "a completely fashioned will," and will may be regarded as an aggregate of tendencies to act in a firm, prompt and definite way upon the principal emergencies of life. A tendency to act only becomes effectively ingrained in proportion to the uninterrupted frequency with which its actions actually occur and the brain becomes adapted to their use. Hence action is paramount since without it effort is sterile.

Man's destiny, according to this view, is in his own

hands. His character, largely fashioned by habit, is malleable and plastic in the early days of life, later it becomes fixed and unalterable. The contemplation of vague intentions and aspirations is useless. It is only by the expenditure of effort translated into action that habitual activity is formed and altered. Here the joint working of physiological mechanisms and psychological processes is clearly manifested.

HABIT AND INSTINCT

Instinctive activity is purposive action in pursuit of ends. There is no foresight of the ends nor is there education in the performance of instinctive action. According to the behaviourist school the conditioned reflex, which is a habit, explains every manifestation of mind and habits are given impulsive powers and result in purposive activity. On the other hand, the hormic theory denies that habit can determine purposive action and holds that habits are but the instruments that are used in the pursuit of ends and are not processes comparable with instinctive activity. Motive, appetite and emotion which are all prominent in instinctive action, are absent in habitual action and the persisting tendency of instinct is in contradistinction to the prompt and automatic reaction of habit.

CHAPTER XIII

INTELLIGENCE

Intelligence, in common with other terms used in psychology, lacks exact definition. In the days of "faculty" psychology intelligence would be thought of as the faculty of the human mind which receives or comprehends the ideas communicated to it. Here intelligence is a synonym for understanding. A description that is more in line with modern thought is that intelligence is the ability to perceive external objects, to conceive of them, to remember, to imagine, to compare, to judge, to abstract and to analyse and to connect thought with thought. Here what is described is not the entity of intelligence but the attributes and functions of the intellectual powers. This description, however, which emphasizes the various aspects of intellect, may be reduced to fall in line with the modern concept of intelligence formulated by Spearman since the common factor involved in the functions of the intellectual process is intelligence itself. Consequently, intelligence may be defined as the factor that is common to all mental abilities. This central factor which is fundamental in all mental operations, is described by Spearman as " G," general ability. This general ability forms the foundation and starting point of all mental abilities. Spearman postulates that " G " may measure the quantity of mental energy approximating to a measure of intelligence. In the same way the perseveration factor " P " may measure the degree of inertia in mental energy. In Spearman's view the individual mental ability is dependent in varying degrees upon the general factor and upon a special ability factor. Essentially, general ability distinguishes relationships and extracts correlates. According to this theory, which is based on statistical and mathematical principles, general ability is more or less equivalent to intelligence and is a measure of the powers of extracting and appreciating relevant relationships.

McDougall holds that the instinctive urges are the prime movers of all human activity and supply the driving power by which all mental activities are sustained. Intelligence here is the servant of the instincts, an instrument which is used in pursuit of instinctive trends.

Glennie formulated as a fundamental law of intellectual development the law of the advance from a quantitatively undetermined to a quantitatively determined conception of the reciprocal action or interaction of all things.

It is generally agreed that intelligence is due to native constitution and is developed by environment and education. Native constitution determined mental ability by fixing limits and by making the individual responsive to certain stimuli. The capacity to improve upon native tendencies is a function of intelligence. It appears clear, however, that heredity determines the degree of intellectual achievement. It is impossible to improve the intelligence of the mental defective beyond a limited standard by either environmental or educational methods.

The term mental defectedness refers traditionally to intellectual defect, a defect in understanding as distinct from emotional abnormality. Intellect in this context connates the ability to understand the environment and the possession of such mental powers that are necessary for self-support. In this connection intelligence is social capacity apart from the educational concept. While mental defect is by common usage referable to intellectual defect or defect of understanding, it is of some importance that the Mental Deficiency Commission of 1932 recognized a continuous curve of variable mental power (intelligence), social capacity and behaviour throughout the range of mental deficiency and progressive to the so-called normal person.

Intelligence in man is inherent and is due to native constitution—as Woodworth remarks—man is an intelligent animal by nature and the fact that he is the most intelligent animal is due to innate constitution since, among the lower animals, some species are more intelligent than others, a difference which is referable to the native constitution. It is clear, however, that members of the same species are not equal in intelligence and the question arises as to whether the difference between members of the same species is due to heredity or environment. While McDougall states that the primary factors in intelligent behaviour are persistence, responsiveness to stimuli and retentiveness and emphasizes the rôle played by the instinct of curiosity, with its attitude of suspended judgment which provides an opportunity to acquire knowledge that is used later in intelligent activity, the term intelligence is frequently applied to the processes of attention, memory and association and, in general, to those intellectual groups of mental attributes that can be refined and cultivated by education and use. On the other hand, intelligence may be restricted to such factors as general ability, mechanical aptitude and social capacity.

While definitions vary in different particulars, the broad view is that intelligence is an innate endowment independent of special instruction that has the capacity of being improved by past experience.

The elucidation of the rival rôles played by heredity and environment in intelligence is assisted by the methods of mental testing.

INTELLIGENCE TESTS

About the year 1900 the educational authorities of Paris required a survey to be made of school children regarding the principles in the ability to learn. The results of this requirement were the Binet-Simon tests for intelligence. These tests are graded in difficulty from three years to twelve years of age and their object was to estimate how high on the scale the child could rank.

It is important to appreciate that the Binet-Simon tests are for general intelligence. The object of all intelligence tests is to look for acquired information and skill and the tests are so arranged and graded that they offer a fairly satisfactory means of assessing general intelligence. Originating in a method of grading school children according to what they actually knew or could do at each level, the tests were evolved by requiring a large number of children to answer questions of varying graduations of difficulty. Those results which were satisfactory were arranged in a series according to the age factor and a number of tests were standardized in such a way that normal children of from three to fifteen years of age should be able to answer the appropriate test group of questions applicable to the actual chronological age.

Since the conception of the Binet-Simon tests for intelligence were evolved there have been several modifications of the original tests. Within recent years the revisions of Terman and Burt, and Terman and Merrill are in general use.

The Binet-Simon tests measure intelligence in terms of mental age. The mental age indicates the intellectual level at any given time. An average normal child of seven years of age has a mental age of seven. Any child whose reactions to the tests obtain the same standard has a mental age of seven irrespective of the actual chronological age.

The intelligence quotient (I.Q.) is arrived at by dividing the mental age by the actual age and multiplying by 100, the intelligence quotient being therefore expressed as a percentage. The intelligence quotient measures brightness or dullness and indicates mental progress.

An intelligence quotient of 90 to 110 shows normal or average intelligence, a quotient of below seventy indicates feeblemindedness and a quotient of below twenty is indicative of idiocy, all figures being approximate. In general, if the child's mental age is the same as his actual age, he is average. If his mental age is above his actual age he is bright and if below he is dull. It follows that the intelligence quotients of the exactly average is 100 per cent, the quotient of the bright child is above 100 per cent, while the quotient of the dull child is below. It is somewhat arbitrarily laid down that an intelligence quotient of less than seventy-five per cent shows mental deficiency.

While the Binet-Simon tests are of the greatest value for practical purposes, it must be realized that they are an educational concept whereas the social point of view is of primary importance. The tests are arbitrary and the method of awarding marks admit the personal factor of the assessor. The assessor requires training in the use of the Binet-Simon scale and quietude and the absence of spectators is essential. The examinee should not be sleepy, the instructions should not be repeated and the child should not be hurried. Praise for the child's endeavours should be given rather than blame and, in general, the factor of the examiner is of considerable importance. The commencement of the tests should be at an age level of one year below the chronological age.

SHORT SUMMARY OF SOME MENTAL TESTS

(*a*) The Dearborn and the Seguin form-board test the perception of form.

(*b*) The Porteous pictorial maze tests, Healy's first and second form-boards, Koh's block test, test attention, perseverance and profiting from experience.

(*c*) The Ebbinghaus story test and Heilbronner's test, test apperception.

(*d*) Raven's progressive matrices, test ability to perceive relationships.

(*e*) Other tests are the absurdity tests, Whipple's word building test, Terman's picture interpretation tests and Munsterberg's test.

(*f*) For very young children. The Terman-Merrill scale. The Merrill-Palmer scale. Gessell's intelligence tests.

(*g*) For the more intelligent adult. The Wechsler-Bellevue intelligence scale. Various group tests of the National Institute of Industrial Psychology.

Mental tests of many varieties have been evolved to test the various attributes of mentality. Their primary objects are comparison both of individuals and of groups and to serve as aids in the estimation of future development. In practice, a battery of mental tests is employed with the object of offsetting the influence of education and for this reason the Binet-Simon tests should be used in conjunction with performance tests since it has been found that poor results in tests of the Binet-Simon type are often accompanied by high results in performance tests. On the other hand a high grading in the Binet-Simon type of tests associated with a low score in performance tests seems to be, in some degree, indicative of temperamental instability.

While there is a considerable diversity of tests for intelligence, tests for the temperamental aspects of the personality are few and perhaps the Rorschact test is the one most generally used. The Rorschact test or "ink blot" consists of presenting a standard series of patterns to the individual and asking him to relate what associations occur to him when he sees them. The associations are coded and classified and their interpretation is standardized.

A method of formulating the results in individuals of the higher intellectual standards lies in placing the individual in appropriate location of the general population examined by the same tests.

This is the percentile method in which results are recorded not in terms of mental age or intelligence quotient but as a percentile rank (Galton). The position is a measure of comparison and is given statistically as a percentile. Thus a percentile rank of thirty indicates that thirty per cent of a population are below and seventy per cent of the same population are above the individual in question, accepting as normal the ranks between twenty-five and seventy-five. Hence a percentile score of eighty-eight indicates that the individual is in the top thirteen per cent of the population as far as intelligence scores on a particular test show.

In general, mental tests should be considered as only one mode of investigation of the mentality. The experience, skill and intuition of the observer are prime factors in mental testing. The important questions of adaptability and social capacity must also receive consideration on drawing conclusions.

CHAPTER XIV

APPERCEPTION AND LANGUAGE

APPERCEPTION

James points out that the word apperception is associated with many different meanings in the evolution of philosophical concepts. Originated by Herbart, the term apperception has been applied to such concepts as interpretation, psychic reaction, conception, assimilation and elaboration.

The process of perception itself is an apperceptive process which includes all recognition, grading and naming and all further thought concerning percepts are apperceptive processes. Apperception connates the sum total of the effects of association and is dependent upon character, habits, memory, education, previous experience and the prevailing mood. It is, however, clear that conceptions are changeable and altered by use. New experiences require correlation with former experiences resulting in alterations in concepts. The mental tendency is to become attached to the old and refuse to admit the new. Established habits of apperception are formed over the years and the individual mind finds it difficult or impossible to change and modify the concepts built up by the impingement of the life situation. James points out that genius in truth means but little more than the faculty of perceiving in an unhabitual way.

Living, as mankind does, in a changing world new concepts are continually intruding and altering former conceptions. When the new is adequately assimilated with the old this achievement gives rise to intellectual pleasure. Before the assimilation is performed the relationship between the old and the new is wonder and is termed by McDougall the primary emotion of the instinct of curiosity. James cogently indicates that neither curiosity nor wonder is experienced concerning things so far beyond us that we have no concepts to refer them to, or standards by which to measure them (e.g. atomic research).

In education it is imperative " to knit every new piece of knowledge on to a pre-existing curiosity, to assimilate its matter in some way to that what is already known. Hence the advantage of comparing all that is far off and foreign to something that is near home, of making the unknown plain by the example of the known, and of connecting all the instruction with the personal experience of the pupil." Only what we partially know already inspires us with the wish to extend our knowledge. It therefore follows that the general law of perception is that while part of what we perceive comes through our senses from the object before us, another part which may be the larger part, always comes out of our own minds.

In physiological terms it would appear that the brain reacts by paths which have been made by previous experience and that these pathways make us perceive the probable thing, which is the thing by which the object is related with the results of previous experience as retained and organized in preformed mental dispositions.

The result of this process is that what is fragmentary is supplemented and expanded and connections are formed for its relatively unconnected parts while the whole is assimilated within the structure of the pre-acquired system of knowledge, belief and imagination.

To summarize, apperception is the successive discernment of the partial features of a single object in relation to each other and in the alterations produced by the modification of old perceptions by new perceptions the structure of a cohesive whole is evolved within the mind.

By the process of apperceptive synthesis the partial is altered into the whole, the disconnected becomes related and the object is associated with the results of previous experience which are retained and organized within the mental dispositions. Without interest the process of apperception is sterile and strange concepts require a sustained effort of attention with resultant difficulty and delay. This blending of the old with the new may involve the appreciation of new sensations and definitely does involve mental work upon identification, interpreting and classifying—a mental effort which brings the object into relationship with previous experience, which supplements the fragmentary, expands and links together the isolated and fits the whole into its niche within the systems of knowledge, imagination and belief previously acquired.

The successive discernment of the partial features of an object in relation to each other is apperceptive synthesis and the use of language prompts the developing mind to effect processes of apperceptive synthesis with a resulting effect on the simplification of language which is reflected in the structure of the mind.

In McDougall's view apperception involves the finding of similarities between objects and classes of objects which have already been distinguished and discriminated from each other. The process of apperception is intrinsically a fusion between two cognitive systems, two systems of cognition amalgamating into one larger system. Here discrimination is the appreciation of differences and apperception is the discovery of similarities. Hence the reproduction of similars is explicit apperception, while intuition is implicit apperception.

In explicit apperception the perception of certain objects results in an impulse to think explicity of certain other objects and to abstract qualities from one object which suggests that another unlikely thing has the same quality. Discrimination of the quality then takes place and the quality is named which leads to the ability to distinguish the quality from the particular object. For example, beauty. The result is that the abstraction of one element from a single object may become applied to a variety of objects or impressions. The total process at work consists of discrimination, apperception and association, all processes that mark the growth of mentality.

Implicit apperception is seen in intuition which is defined by McDougall as a subtle conjunction of sense impressions that are beyond analysis but which determines the conative-emotional reaction. The logical structure of the mind results from discrimination and apperception and, in essence, is the appreciation of differences and similarities of qualities and the things to which qualities are attached.

LANGUAGE

The use of language leads the developing mind to effect processes of apperceptive synthesis and thus a simplification of language was produced which reflects a simplification of the structure of the mind. Replacing separate names for every class of objects which are in their implications inherently similar, names have been evolved for larger classes of objects which are comprised of objects which are similar in some respects although these aspects are not so obvious or so immediately and practically important. As a result the classification of the animal world has been graded by successive apperceptions which have discovered homologies and have resulted in the present scientific classification. Hence apperceptive synthesis is a principal factor in the higher development of the intellect which, by its aid, may find remote resemblances, analogies, homologies, similes and metaphors. Apperceptive synthesis in this view forms a characteristic factor in the higher level of mental processes.

Words are language symbols and as the mind develops so does language become more complicated and includes thinking activity and ultimately symbolizes highly complex mental processes. Language symbols are governed by association as are perceptional images, and words that are connected by similarity and associated temporally are revived together. But here the meaning of the word has also to be considered and words become associated through their meanings. This association by the similarity of meaning is a mental development of great importance since it provides the mechanism of intellectual activity. Intelligent directed thought is a process by which word images are rearranged and new associations are formed according to the meanings attached to the words. This association by similarity of meaning is a mental achievement of profound significance alluded to by Johnson as "an inspiration, the brain's livery servant; the dress of thought." The social and national importance of language is obvious since the national mind is reflected in the national speech for, if the way which men express their thoughts is slipshod and mean, it is difficult for their thoughts themselves to escape being the same. A national reputation for simplicity and truthfulness cannot be maintained when the language is high-flown and bombastic.

Stout maintains that language is an instrument of conceptual analysis and synthesis. By the process of analysis, the concrete details of actual sense perception is fragmented and certain aspects are selected which have a general or conceptual character. By conceptual synthesis the partial aspects are recombined into a new whole. In all trains of ideational thinking the several parts become definite and determinate by their relations within the ideal whole which is being constructed. Hence concrete sense perception is replaced by conceptual synthesis, as Hegel remarked, thought passes always from the abstract to the concrete.

In language the predominating factor is the mode of mental activity involved. This is based on experience and language is a means by which ideal analysis of objects and processes into common factors which may be reconstructed on the lines of past experience and thus form the foundation of common meaning.

To summarize the factors in the evolution of language it has been seen that by conceptual analysis perceptions are broken up and, from the the fragmentation, general aspects are selected, each aspect originating a series of comparisons in which there is a common abstract factor which explicitly distinguishes the unity of the thing from its various qualities. Conceptual synthesis assimilates the partial aspects in a new whole and at the same time aids the distinguishing of relationships and differences. While conceptual thinking is the discernment of the general from the particular by the use of language, attention is concentrated on universal factors as distinguished from percepts. Hence language is an instrument of conceptual analysis since the signs inherent in a linguistic system are individually connected with some universal aspect of concrete experience and the attention exercises a selective activity on the universal in distinction from the particular and recalls the universal when it is mentally reproduced or again perceived. Language, therefore, stabilizes the results of conceptual analysis and synthesis and in its function as a mode of communication prompts and controls conceptual synthesis and analysis in others.

Language develops from the primitive system of natural signs and visible gestures. By the evolution of oral language, universals or general aspects are expressed and attention may be fixed on general aspects as distinguished from percepts. Originally produced spontaneously, sounds later are prompted by imitation. Primitive sounds are the expression of the emotions and of organic sensations, but later the universal becomes differentiated from the particular by the analysis and selection of special aspects of perception which are recombined and associated in words which characterize a complete situation and absent objects are ideally represented by means of their universal characteristics and an ideally represented whole results.

THEORIES OF THE ORIGIN OF LANGUAGE

While McDougall states that the primary function of language is to create preperception by expectation or prior thinking of an object before perceiving it, the majority of the theories of the origin of language are concerned with the evolution of conventional signs from natural signs. That ideas are transferred by selecting characteristic features of objects and by the means of expressive noises and signs communicating them to others is the onomatopoeic theory which has its basis in a process of mimicry and imitation. The interjectional theory maintains that language arose from the expression of emotional activity while the pathognomic theory postulates that language originated from the fact that specific objects so affect man as to evoke correspondingly specific utterances depending upon a harmony of sound and sense. In these theories the primary factor is that natural science preceded conventional science and ultimately resulted in the creation of speech. Stigmatized by Muller as the Pooh Pooh, the Bow Wow and the Ding Dong, these theories exclude visible gesture and are only concerned with vocal signs. In Stout's view the starting point is the visible gesture.

THE DEVELOPMENT OF LANGUAGE

Primarily, the infant produces various spontaneous sounds which after a while are prompted by imitation and which are the expressions of the emotions and of organic sensation. Following this stage, the child obtains pleasure from the motor activity of the larynx, tongue and lips. Later, the growing child, by analysis distinguishes the universal from the particular and ideally represents absent objects by means of their universal characteristics. As mentality develops fixed associations are formed between the name and the features which are common to a variety of objects. The final stage is the combination of words by the process of conceptual synthesis into a context which is symbolic of the complex situation. Here, education and the evolution of language, as Arnold pointed out with reference to Greek and Latin, is instrumental in forming the human mind in youth. Nothing is of more importance in the relationships of differing psychological mentalities than the use of words. Far from being a mere exercise of grammarians, words have a meaning which is indicative of the progress made in civilization. It is in the abuse of words that the limits of vice and virtue become ill-defined and it is in the precise definition of words that society advances towards a higher civilization.

CHAPTER XV

IMITATION AND SUGGESTION

IMITATION

It has been said that imitation is the sincerest form of flattery, but imitation leads mankind to leave natural ways and to enter into artificial modes of conduct. Fontaine remarked that imitators are a servile race and it is reported of Plato that, being crooked-shouldered, his scholars, who much admired him, would endeavour to be like him by bolstering out their garments on that side. The commentator, with some wit, observed that it was probable that his students found it easier to imitate Plato's shoulders than his philosophy and to stuff their gowns rather than to furnish their understandings.

McDougall considers that the meaning of the word imitate may well be extended to the process of suggestion since imitation, a term used by Tarde to include processes of suggestion and sympathy, is descriptive of the mental state of the subject of suggestion. Strictly, however, imitation is only applicable to the imitations of the actions and bodily movements of someone else. James includes imitations under instinctive activity and refers to the first impulse to imitate in connection with the learning of walking in children. McDougall does not recognize imitation as an instinct because of the variety of imitative actions and because of their lack of specificity. In addition, a congenital disposition is not involved in imitation nor is there any common impulse or affective state seeking satisfaction.

While McDougall distinguishes three principal varieties of imitative action, primitive sympathy, ideomotor actions, as in hypnosis and latah, and deliberate imitation of admired personalities, he places the main emphasis of imitation within the province of social life, pointing out that imitation moulds the growing individual and assimilates him to the type of society into which he is born. Imitation in this view determines to a large extent the operations of the collective or the community mind, its collective deliberations, emotions, character and volition.

The superiority of man over other animals is due to the greater power of learning, of profiting by experience and of acquiring new modes of adjustment and reaction. Physiologically man's superiority would seem to be due to the possession of a very large brain which implies a considerable capacity for adaptation and adjustment. The size of the brain and the accompanying adjustment facilities would appear to have been developed *pari-passu* with the development of community life and with the evolution of language, the great agent and promoter of social life. The culture which typifies civilization, the growth of morality and of intellectual capacity, the mental storage of knowledge, belief and custom results in a tradition which constitutes one of the pillars of society. All tradition, however, exists only by virtue of imitation since it is by imitation that each successive generation acquires the tradition of the preceding age. Hence, imitation is not only the conservative force in society but is also essential to all social progress.

According to Stout, imitation may be described as a conation seeking satisfaction in the imitative impulse itself. In its more complex forms it presupposes trains of ideas but, essentially, it is present and operates at the perceptual level. Stout distinguishes between the ability to imitate and the impulse to imitate. Sometimes there may be learning by imitation with little or no impulse to imitate. Here the imitative process is enacted not for its own sake but because of some ulterior motive. The imitative impulse itself, the impulse to perform an action which arises from the perception of it as performed by someone else, is associated with attentive consciousness. Automatic imitation, however, requires to be distinguished from the imitative impulse. Automatic imitation may be due to habitual association or may be due to a general habit of doing as others do where there is no need to act to the contrary. In the latter, the factors involved in the automatic impulse are economy of time and trouble, in so much as it is easier to follow a collective example, dislike of attracting attention by going against the general procedure and the factor of experience which teaches that what others do is often based upon good reason.

The imitative impulse, however, is a conation which is satisfied by its own operation. Interest is necessary for the attainment of full gratification and to imitate an action means that the action imitated must have personal interest value. Here attention shows it striving for a definite, vivid and more complete apprehension of the object. Interest, however, may be primary or acquired through prior experience. In young animals and children interest is primary and dependent on congenital tendencies. In general, an action is imitated only when there is an independent tendency to perform it and actions that are alien to the personality are normally not imitated. It is for this reason, amongst others, that an instinct of imitation cannot be recognized.

In the learning of children and animals it is sometimes difficult to distinguish the rôles played by imitation and by observation. Learning by imitation usually resolves itself, on further inquiry, into a learning by observation and often the so-called delayed imitation is, in reality, a learning by observation followed by trial and error. McDougall points out that imitation in animals is a simple following which is initiated by the gregarious impulse and by primitive passive sympathy. In learning by imitation the power to imitate is proportional to the power of performing the same kind of action. Imitation may improve the power of learning but it cannot create the power. Where learning is aided by imitation mental plasticity must be adequate for the imitative impulse to show results. Where mental development has reached its higher levels there is a tendency for the imitative impulse to be impeded by activity organized within a unified system and hence imitation in these circumstances is evoked as an aid to the achievement of ulterior motives.

The importance of imitation in the development of self-consciousness has previously been dealt with and it only remains necessary to emphasize the ramifications of the conative urge of imitation in the building up of the mentality in learning, in language, in social tradition and in the concept of the self.

SUGGESTION

Belief may become established by one of three methods, by reason, by intuition and by suggestion. In the rational method the facts are examined and a logical conclusion is reached on the evidence presented. This logical process, where the conscious mind perceives circumstances as they really are and not in the added light of subjective and objective factors, emotions and sentiments which distort perceptions and compromise judgments, is the ideal mode of establishing belief. In belief, which has been arrived at by intuition, reason is disregarded and judgment is passed aided by the emotions and by implicit apperception.

In the reacting organism the stimulus to reaction should be followed by the thought process and the reaction is delayed until the thought process has evolved a judgment which is the conscious foundation of the reaction. The principle at work is that thought is essentially directed towards action. Where the thought process does not take place, the ensuing type of reaction is instinctive or conditioned by emotion and is impulsive, a direct response to a perception. The tendency here is to produce a false judgment, and should the emotional state at the time be of some strength, it impedes both thought and action. Therefore, for logical belief to become established and motivate appropriate action, logical analysis, which is basically the production of the relevant associations, must take place. In suggestion there is implicit belief in the written or spoken word. Mental investigation does not take place, the necessary logical mental associations are not formed and belief is established by suggestion.

One of the best definitions of suggestion is that of McDougall who postulated that suggestion was a process of communication resulting in the acceptance with conviction of the communicated proposition independently of the subject's appreciation of any logical grounds for its acceptance. Only hetero-suggestion is recognized by this definition, auto-suggestion being neglected.

The liability to accept any proposition conveyed is the condition of suggestibility and the process of communication is suggestion. The degree of suggestibility is the measurement of the readiness with which propositions are accepted. The degree of suggestibility varies according to the topic and according to the source suggesting the proposition and also according to the state of mentality from time to time. Suggestibility is low in individuals with organized systems of knowledge and where the critical attitude is sustained by interrelating systems of belief. Suggestibility may be high in those mental conditions of relative dissociation found in such states as hysteria, sleep and fatigue and greater degrees of suggestibility are commonly found in individuals whose mental equipment is unorganized but, probably, the most important factors in increased suggestibility is the impressiveness of the source of suggestion and the innate character and native disposition of the individual. The latter factor includes the relative strengths of the two instincts of self-submission and self-assertion. The general emotional attitude towards those individuals regarded as superior is one of submission, to those regarded as inferior is one of self-assertion. Where the sentiment of self-regard is well developed, suggestibility is weak.

It would appear probable that the basis of suggestion is related to inhibitions which impede the mind from commencing the necessary processes of associating the new idea or perception with the aggregation of previous mental experiences and to the presence of an affective, emotional or sentimental disposition which is aroused at the same time as the new idea or perception enters consciousness.

It has been seen that the essential element in reasoning

is association and therefore factors which hinder association, such as inhibition, lead to a state of dissociation which influences the criteria of belief and leads to a train of consequences that culminate in the motor and sensory manifestations of hysteria.

In McDougall's view, suggestion is conditioned by the impulse of the submissive instinct and it is from the energy within the instinct of submission that suggestion draws its driving power. This energy is evoked and directed by the influence of suggestion, by the hypnotist, by the person of prestige, by the parents, the teachers, the journalists and the advertisers and, perhaps increasingly, by those in power and by those to whom mankind turns for spiritual guidance. It has been well said that we often believe what our fathers believed before us without searching into the reason of our belief. There are but few sublime wits that pry into the origin of things.

Woodworth distinguishes between suggestion exercised by a person and suggestion which arises as a result of the circumstances. Personal suggestion in this context is almost entirely a matter of prestige but suggestion which is exercised by the circumstances is "auto-suggestion," an entity which, in spite of Coué, who maintained that all suggestion is auto-suggestion, is debatable.

Other definitions of suggestion are those of Janet who held that suggestion was the complete and automatic development of an idea which takes place outside the will and personal perception of the subject. This definition was criticized by Babinski who pointed out that the suggested idea must be unreasonable since, if it be reasonable, the process involved is one of persuasion. Hart postulated that the essential process in suggestion is the inhibition of conflicting ideas. Myers held that suggestion was a successful appeal to the subliminal consciousness. Sidis stated that suggestion was an intrusion into the mind of an idea which is met with more or less opposition by the subject, accepted at last and realized automatically and unreflectively.

The psychoanalysts regard hypnosis as an artificially induced hysteria and postulate the unconscious indentification of the operator with a parent. On the other hand, Salter suggests that all hypnotic phenomena are conditioned reflexes.

The definitions and explanations of suggestion are numerous and varied but the intrinsic factors in suggestion are moderately clear and in any theory of suggestion regard must be given to the innate constitution, the mode in which the mind has been organized, the influence of instinctive energy and, paramountly, to the prestige and esteem involved in the suggestive influence.

METHODS OF APPLYING SUGGESTION

There are four principal methods of applying suggestion. (1) By hypnotism. Hypnotism increases the degree of suggestibility. It is of use in hysteria and in the recall of memory losses. (2) Sleeping suggestion is particularly applicable to children. Suggestions may be whispered into the ear of the sleeping child and are acted upon in the waking state. This method is useful in the treatment of enuresis. (3) Waking suggestion. Here relaxation in the subject is an essential. Jacobsen has shown the importance of complete muscular relaxation in the treatment of emotional tension. (4) Hypnoidization is a state of relaxation and composure during which suggestions are made. In all essentials it is similar to waking suggestion.

It will be seen that suggestion is a most useful form of treatment in the psychoneuroses and particularly in hysteria. In the treatment of amnesia hyposis is of value in reviving dormant memories and in the treatment of amnesic blocks. In alcoholism, drug addiction and in insomnia suggestion plays a part in treatment.

FACTORS INFLUENCING SUGGESTIBILITY

(a) Age. McDougall has pointed out that in children where the operation of the submissive instinct is marked, suggestibility is prominent, since the adult must know better than the child. When the mind becomes less plastic, as in old age, suggestion has but limited opportunities.

Rapport, the assuming of the parental attitude by the operator, increases suggestibility.

(b) Prestige. Suggestions are much more readily received from individuals who have prestige and authority in the eyes of the subject. Confidence in the operator is essential and every means should be used to enhance prestige and reputation. It is in the assumption of the parental attitude that trust, respect and love is developed. An essential factor in the giving of suggestion is full confidence in the ability to employ this method. Domination not domineering, commanding not supplicating, compelling not asking are requisites of the skilled operator. An atmosphere of mystery and ritual reinforces suggestion in some instances.

(c) Frequency. The more frequently suggestion is given the more suggestible the subject becomes. Faith and belief in the personality and powers of the operator are essential to achieve good results. This action of frequency and repetition is also seen in the psychology of advertising. Discipline is allied to frequency and a subject who has served in a disciplined capacity is particularly liable to the influence of suggestion.

Propaganda and its dependence upon suggestion requires some mention. Sidis alludes to suggestibility as "the cement of the herd." In propaganda the aim is to alter the opinions of the members of the herd by suggestion and so to modify their actions.

Propaganda inherently depends upon the submissive propensity and upon primitive passive sympathy. The herd instinct and the instinct of escape with its primary emotion of fear are here essentially involved. In propaganda the submissive impulse is exploited together with the attributes of the herd instinct and the inherent factors in suggestion.

In community attitudes in which the rôle of submission predominates propaganda finds an opportunity to sway and create public opinion. Here the populous are influenced by the power principle since those in power must be acquainted with the facts of the situation. In propaganda distortion of facts is inevitable if the objects of propaganda are to be achieved. It is upon the twin factors of submission and suggestibility that propaganda produces its results.

Propaganda can only be combated by the integrity of mutually supporting systems of belief, by the influence of personal logical judgments which appreciate the distortion of facts and by the erection of mutually supporting and cohesive systems of personal beliefs.

Logical judgment should independently assess the facts, the interrelationship of insight and knowledge should estimate the consequences of the situation and the implications of the facts should be weighed in their personal relationship with the aggregation of experience and with the extent of personal knowledge.

CHAPTER XVI

SLEEP AND DREAMS

Sleep

There are many theories which seek to explain the phenomena of sleep but none are entirely satisfactory and no final conclusion can yet be reached. Sleep is "no servant of the will" and neither psychological or physiological theories are able to provide more than tentative explanations of this periodic withdrawal from reality, this intermittent inactivity of the cerebral cortex.

The outward or physical changes displayed in the sleeping state are clear. Although there is no evidence of cerebral anaemia, a former popular theory, there is a fall in the blood pressure and a slowing of the heart rate. The carbon dioxide tension in the arterial blood is raised while the metabolic rate is lowered. There is increased elimination of acid and ammonium salts, a relaxation of skeletal muscle and, because of this loss of tone the deep reflexes are in abeyance. The knee jerk and the normal plantar reflex is absent. The Babinski response indicates that the discharge from the motor cortex is absent. The pupils are contracted and the light reflex is preserved. The cortical electrical rhythms as shown by electro-encephalography display the delta waves, slow random waves which are associated with states of cortical inactivity.

Theories of Sleep

Pavlov maintained that natural sleep is due to widespread "active" internal inhibition. Pavlov reached this view in his attempts to explain the onset of sleep during his conditioned reflex experiments. Koch demonstrated that afferent impulses from the carotid sinuses may result in cortical inhibition and a condition undistinguishable from sleep. The objection to these views is that sleep cannot be regarded as an acquired process such as conditioned reflexes.

Wright points out that it may be possible that the primary condition of the brain is one of sleep and that wakefulness is dependent upon afferent stimuli. This view is in line with Economo's "sleep centre" theory which postulates a sleep centre to be situated in the grey matter surrounding the third ventricle and the aqueduct of Sylvius. Should this be the case, the centre would, in reality, control wakefulness. Hess suggested that there is a subcortical centre controlling both the sleeping and waking states. Hess maintained that sleep is conditioned by parasympathetic activity and is, in fact, a state of vagotonia. During sleep there is a fall in the blood calcium and it has been suggested that this is due to the concentration of calcium in the brain. A practical point which emerges from this observation (Demole) is that calcium and sedative drugs should be administered in combination.

Amongst psychological theories of sleep that have been advanced that of McDougall requires consideration. McDougall regards sleep as a minor instinct and postulates an instinct to relax, rest and sleep. McDougall agrees with Claparède that this instinctive view of sleep is strongly supported by the analogy between normal sleep and the hibernating sleep of animals which is probably instinctive in character. Further, the fact that the powers of sleeping and waking at will—a power that can be cultivated, would seem to give additional support to this view. Napoleon wrote: "different matters are arranged in my head as in drawers; I open one drawer and close another as I wish. I have never been kept awake by an involuntary preoccupation of the mind. If I desire repose, I shut up all the drawers and sleep. I have always slept when I wanted rest and almost at will." Wright emphasizes the fact that to produce an efferent discharge a continual afferent drive is usually needed. "The preparation for sleep reduce the sensory stream to a minimum level: the quiet room, the closed eyes and the relaxation of the muscles all reduce the incoming impulses from the dominant distance receptors and also from the proprioceptors. We may suppose that in absence of an adequate afferent stream cerebral activity is suspended.'' It will be noted that the above description contains a majority of the marks of behaviour, preparation, persistence, retentivity, totality and purpose and that preparatory reactions and persistence, variations and modifications by experience, universality and remoteness of the goal, as compared with reflex action, are indicative of instinctive behaviour.

The view that sleep is an instinctive response to a drowsy state and that going to sleep is a definite act is also held by Woodworth who points to the native preparatory reactions displayed. It would seem probable that sleep is an instinctive activity designed to prevent exhaustion but not conditioned by exhaustion. In the infant, sleep has all the appearance of instinctive behaviour but, as mental development increases, sleep may become modified by voluntary mental factors. Other factors such as suggestion and confidence may also alter sleep.

DREAMS

Sensations are objective immediate experiences. Mental images, the revivals or copies of sensational experience, are also objective immediate experiences. Stout points out that a characteristic of objective immediate experience is privacy which is particularly marked in hallucinations and dreams. Here the sensations which are ordinarily experienced in perceiving certain objects are experienced in the absence of these objects. Immediate experiences are not shared in common by different minds since each individual experiences his own sensations and appreciates them in his own particular way. Hence the difficulty in adequately appreciating the dreams of others since the unity of experience is the unity of different modes of consciousness which are personal, private and individual phases in the life history of the personal consciousness. The intrinsic characteristics of these modes of consciousness cannot be shared. They may, to some limited extent, be explained but the explanations lack the colour, detail and vividness of the dream experience as it is appreciated by the dreamer. Further, those private and personal factors which enrich the dream content by linkage with the personality attributes of the dreamer are, to some extent, absent in the relation of the dream. Hence, as will be seen, many difficulties are encountered in the accurate interpretation of dreams.

Any sensory stimulus may give origin to a dream. The nightmare of the dyspeptic, "child of the night of indigestion bred," arises from organic sensation. The noise of the wind, the ticking of a clock, the creaking of the stairs may be sensory stimuli that initiate dreaming. In these cases the dream is an illusion, a false perception. Sometimes the dream is an hallucination arising from a train of thought and images that have but little connection with present sensory stimuli. Touch and pressure stimuli, cold and heat sensations, any state of uncomfortable tension may give rise to dreams and, as Ladd pointed out, the excitement of the retina by internal conditions is a potent source of dream determination.

The stimulus that arouses dream thoughts is usually converted into a visual picture. There is no auditory image nor does speech take place in dreams, but there is interchange of thought. "In dreams we hear no sound unless it be those of the world without. We carry on many conversations and marvellous things are told us; but these, like our waking communings with ourselves, are uttered by voiceless lips in a speechless tongue. Dreamland is a silent land and all the dwellers in it are deaf and dumb." Dream thought is illogical and inconsistent, often fantastic, grotesque and incoherent. Frequently the dream may be simply a free play of the imagination and the seeming reality of dreams arise from the fact that images are accepted as real. Judgment, criticism, and reasoning are suspended and the stimulus arouses a series of thoughts and images which are symbolic of the stimulus itself. In this connection a dream is an example of apperception.

During sleep, reality is excluded, but mentation continues in the form of dreams and, since in sleep, all the senses have an equal opportunity, impressions from them are not so liable to be overlooked as during waking. Herodotus remarked that dreams in general take their rise from those incidents which have occurred during the day and this is often true since the stimulus which arouses the dream by night has been unnoted during the day, a further example of the persistence of conation.

While dreams probably have some individual significance as is shown by recurrent dreams, consideration of these aspects requires an understanding of Freud's theory of dreams.

Freud conceived the dream to be always the picture of a wish-fulfilment, the wish being conscious or unconscious and often unsatisfied or repressed. The dream content as recollected by the subject of the dream is the manifest content. The latent content consists of the unconscious processes by which the manifest content has been built up, in other words, the latent content of the dream is the wishes, impulsive desires or ideas of which the dream is the manifest but disguised expression. The dream work is the method of transformation utilized upon the unconscious material, methods which alter the latent content into the manifest content. These methods consist of condensation, symbolization, displacement, dramatization, regression and secondary elaboration.

Condensation converts the latent content into the "condensed" content of the manifest dream by a process of blending together or telescoping several latent elements with a common characteristic into one dream symbol which represents several persons or dream factors. Alternatively, a single object may be represented by a number of symbols. By symbolization is meant that many of the elements in the manifest content are symbols of fairly constant value for elements in the latent content. Many dream symbols like coach, king, queen, dance and so on are standard symbols for persons or impulses, the ideas of which are commonly repressed. Displacement is the mechanism whereby the attached affect or emotion connected with ideas, persons or things is transferred to some apparently unrelated object, persons or situation. Dramatization results in a heightening of the value of conflicts by altering and adding to the matter of the manifest content dramatic incidents and details as when the individual is confronted by some small difficulty and it becomes magnified into a calamity in the dream. Regression is a term used descriptive of returning to the days of childhood and dreams that show regression are on the lines of fairy stories whose characters are simple and obvious. Secondary elaboration takes place between waking and recording the dream. In this connection, it is important to record in writing all dreams immediately on waking since much distortion and addition is usually shown later.

Freud considered that in all individuals there were many wishes which were opposed to the personality and so repugnant to the individual that expression of them was only possible in a distorted and symbolized form in dreams. These wishes, forming the basis of the dreams, required expression in a form that is acceptable to the personality even in the dream stage. By the analysis of dream material the basic wish may be elucidated to the conscious mind and appreciated and dealt with.

In fear and anxiety dreams, where "the weak are dreaming endless fears," recall of a past fear stimulus may be made by association but Freud regards fear as a symbolic representation of a positive desire which is at variance with the personality and which finds expression as anxiety.

Wish fulfilment dreams are common in children and here, are the direct, unsymbolized fulfilment of a wish. During sleep the conscious level of the mind is dormant and the unconscious mind is then free to assert itself and wishes that have been repressed into the unconscious evade the moral and social standards of the adult and manifest themselves in symbolized and disguised forms. Hence the unconscious finds an expression in dreams which are the keys to the contents of the unconscious. It must be noted, however, that the self-assertive impulse may obtain its only satisfaction in the dream state.

Freud's theory of dreams has been criticized on the grounds that suppressed wishes are not so universally unconscious and it has been held that it is not so much the unconscious wish that is expressed in dreams as the conscious but unsatisfied wish. Again, Freud's theory does not valuate the self-assertion tendency adequately. Self-assertion in community life must, in many aspects be suppressed and may give rise to dreams in which it finds expression.

Jung does not limit the meaning of dreams to wish fulfilment and he regards dreams as an attempt to solve a more immediate and practical problem. Here the dream has a purposive action and deals with the present difficulties of the dreamer and is an indication of the path taken by the personality to resolve its difficulties.

CHAPTER XVII

THE UNCONSCIOUS MIND

The theory of an unconscious portion of the mind was the subject of psychological debate prior to Freud's concept of the unconscious mind. The co-conscious of Morton Prince postulated the operation of separate processes continuing within the personality, the main personality being unaware of the activities of the secondary personality. Charcot and Janet in 1881 showed that during the process of hypnotism forgotten memories could be recalled under hypnosis and that the revival of memories was impeded by inhibitions which prevented their entry into consciousness but did not obstruct their activity and their influence on behaviour. In addition, hypnosis showed that emotions, desires and wishes could be prevented from entering consciousness by inhibition. These investigations pointed to the postulate that some portion of the mind lay beyond consciousness and that unconscious process eventuated without the conscious appreciation of the individual. It appeared that the working of instinctive activity, the flow of emotional manifestations, the persistence of striving, were but dimly appreciated, if at all, by the individual consciousness and yet these factors told upon conscious life as in James's phrase "light upon the landscape."

It was not until Freud elaborated his theory of the unconscious mind that the essential importance of these mental factors was appreciated. That the mind contained elements which were not accessible to consciousness had previously been suspected but it was Freud who was the first to clearly recognize that these factors were in a state of disharmony with the rest of the mind. As Jones cogently wrote, "by the technique which Freud employed, the most deeply buried constituents of the mind were exposed and the conception of the mind became radically altered."

In 1895, Freud and Breuer, as a result of their studies of the phenomena of hypnosis, postulated that unconscious processes were an essential factor in mental life and that the mind could be compared ,to a series of watertight compartments between which communication is actively impeded by definite factors. These factors, which were opposed to the subject's becoming aware of certain portions of his mind, Freud named resistances which were later termed repressions. Both the resistances and the part of the mind they are opposed to are beyond the individual's consciousness and it is for this reason that Freud uses the term unconscious (in German, *das Umbewusste;* literally, "the unapprehended"). Freud pursued the study of unconscious activity and because of the limitations of hypnosis he elaborated a new method of mental investigation which was named psychoanalysis. As a result of this new concept Freud regards the mind as being capable of stimulation from without and from within and he figuratively distinguished three layers of mind, the conscious mind, the subconscious or preconscious and the unconscious.

The conscious mind, according to this conception, is concerned with all the thoughts that one is aware of at any moment of time. The conscious includes all the experiences that are actually being presented and, according to their distance from the focus of attention, such experiences are in varied degrees of clearness. Below the conscious mind is the subconscious or preconscious in which are the thoughts that can become conscious should the circumstances warrant. The memories stored in the subconscious are those memories or thoughts that may be readily revived and become conscious and those thoughts and memories that require much effort to become conscious. There is probably an association between these and the contents of the unconscious. The deepest layer of all is the unconscious whose contents are entirely incapable of becoming conscious except under analysis.

The subconscious mind results in part from repression, the process of dismissing from consciousness trends that are at variance with the personality or with the life circumstances. The subconscious, containing as it does, childish and infantile propensities, wishes, emotions and desires, chiefly instinctive in origin, is only concerned with the individual's egoistical trends which are largely the satisfaction of instinctive urges. The subconscious mind is not concerned with morality, ethics or reason, it is the repository of those primitive desires and emotions that comprise the instinctive make-up of the individual and, since instinct is an urge to action, the subconscious seeks expression of its contents with total disregard of any other factors.

It has been seen that academic psychology referred to the ego as the concept of the self derived from a recombination of abstractions from many individualities and essentially conditioned by physical sensations. Superimposed upon this physical basis which conveys the idea of the material bodily self there are the many aspects of the self, the self knowing, experiencing, striving and feeling and the ego is expanded and formulated upon the reconstruction of abstractions from these many selves. Primarily, the ego is subjective being the subject of knowledge, but when the self thinks of itself the ego becomes objective as in self-criticism. James defines the ego as a collection of cephalic movements or adjustments which, for want of attention and reflection, usually fail to be perceived and to this is added a feeling of something more, thought becoming its own object. The mental attributes that differentiate one person from another are personal experiences and the mode of reaction to past experiences. The ego, according to this view, is a feeling comprising all the feelings of the moment with the addition of all the feelings of the past.

Freud's conception of the ego is that it is the entity which basically establishes relations between the organism and the environment. The ego is the conscious, rational mind. Previously, Freud postulated a selective agency which he called the censor which operated between the subconscious and the deep unconscious. Later, however, Freud's concept of the superego was formulated and replaced the censor.

The superego is evolved during the course of development and is chiefly unconscious. While the superego is in close relationship to the deep unconscious, it exercises a vigilance over material that is repressed and is the factor which dictates what is to be repressed. The repressive process is conditioned by the childish standards of the individual regarding morality and is not influenced by the results of education and experience. Hence repression, a cardinal feature in Freud's theory, is carried out on the standards not of the adult mind but upon those of childhood. The superego is dictatorial, excessively moral and intolerant.

While the repressed impulses are those that conflict with the moral and social standards of the individual, it must be appreciated that the process of repression itself is unconscious and therefore has not been exposed to a conscious moral judgment. Freud conceives the nature of the repressed impulses to be almost entirely sexual in character and postulates that it is the function of the superego to act as a moral guardian of the mind. Where the superego lacks proper developmental sequence this deficiency may result in the evolution of various forms of mental disorder.

Theoretically, the superego is the unconscious continuation of beliefs and moral standards that have survived from the early infantile days of the individual and which have not been altered by the impingement of experience and example upon the personality. In childhood, the rationale of right and wrong, the growth of moral principles and the estimation of the individuality is definite and permits but little deviations. The standards of the child are retained in the operation of the superego which is not influenced by reason or by that indulgent tolerance which the adult mind displays. In this relationship the impulse of aggression has a principal place, for should the aggressive impulses be denied their normal external satisfaction, aggression becomes introjected and ultimately develops into a factor that may culminate in ideas of inferiority and of guilt.

Instinctive images and primordial impulses lie in the deeper layers of the mind. These impulses are unconscious and have no personality but are continually seeking satisfaction. Since this part of the mind is purely impersonal, Freud calls it the id or it and conceives it to be the origin of mental energy derived from the instincts. These unconscious processes are governed entirely by the pleasure-pain principle and the energy inherent within them is capable of being utilized by any of the instinctive cravings. It is the function of psychoanalysis to uncover and bring to light these unconscious motives which have such a profound influence on mentality. The id seeks satisfaction at all costs. Entirely concerned with the gratification of its inherent propensities, morality and ethics are disregarded and infantile trends and primitive urges seek their goal with entire want of attention to the penalty which may result from the achievement of their ends.

It is the function of the conscious ego to interpose between conflicting desires, to hold its mediate position as an adjustor to the insistent claims of the id, to the moral demands of the superego and to the exigencies of reality.

Here it is appropriate to depict Freud's meaning of sexuality since much of the opposition that has been manifested to Freud's conceptions and to psycholanalysis as a mode of treatment in mental disorders has originated from this topic. Freud holds that the sexual instinct is present in the first year of life and from this state of infantile sexuality passes through a series of phases in the next three years. A cardinal principles of Freud's theory of sexuality is that the development of the sexual instinct may be fixated, arrested or deflected at any of the phases. As the child passes through these developmental stages the child's affective relationship to his parents and the conflicts arising in connection with them may profoundly affect the individual's character in adult life. The mode by which the child deals with these incestuous trends is of great importance and since repressions and sublimations may be precarious and sometimes inadequate processes, the attitude of the parents towards the child is of the utmost import.

It must be constantly recollected that these conflicts at an early stage of development are, at the time, mostly unconscious and are generally forgotten in later life. In them Freud distinguishes the roots of mental disturbances and he states that the Oedipus complex is the source of all neuroses.

Should two groups of mutually conflicting impulses be stimulated at the same time the ensuing situation is termed a conflict. Conflicts arise particularly in relationship to instinctive tendencies. One tendency is repressed and its affective cognitive disposition becomes dispersed. Where the sentiments exist in well-organized and mutually supporting systems, the tendency to conflict becomes inevitably more marked. Freud was of the opinion that the affective cognitive dispositions becomes dissociated without resolution. Where this happens the dissociated affective disposition is termed a complex. The complex becomes dissociated from the personality and, not being admitted to consciousness, is said to be restricted with reference to the repressed material. Because of the activities of the superego the complex is unable to take part in conscious life and as it is continually seeking satisfaction it may obtain a partial gratification by manifesting itself in dreams or in the symptoms of mental disorder.

When the flow of interest in one direction is blocked by the process of repression it may be deflected into other channels by which the tension of complexes may be released and the energy which is attached to instinctive activity may be expended without detriment to the personality in activity which is of use. This is the process of sublimation by which a substitute satisfaction is obtained and the libido is expended advantageously. The process of sublimation operates unconsciously and varies in strength in different individuals. Sublimation is of the utmost importance in the development of mentality and from it springs the higher sentiments and the evolution of civilization, morality, ethical codes and the arts and sciences—in fact, the process of sublimation provides the driving force for the many and complex achievements of the human mind. Sublimation to some degree can be aided by moral and ethical training and it is the function of education to provide new channels for the dispersion of the vital energy inherent in the innate instinctive equipment.

It will have been noted that Freud's views have been built up from the conception of the unconscious being the origin of mental energy derived from the instincts. Freud named this general instinctive energy the libido and differing radically from other schools of psychological theory regarded the libido as subserving the sexual instinct only. That the libido during the process of development may be directed, attached or fixated in different ways according to the evolution of the sexual instinct is the cardinal point in Freud's concept. The emphasis here, however, is upon two points in Freud's psychology, the nature of the libido and the rôle played by the unconscious mind. In order to arrive at some conclusions regarding the influence of the unconscious mind upon mental life the views of Jung must also receive consideration.

JUNG'S ANALYTICAL PSYCHOLOGY

Jung was the founder of the Zürich school of psychology and was formerly a disciple of Freud. It is to Jung that psychologists are indebted for a concise statement of what Freud means by sexuality and for pointing out that Freud's concept of sexuality is utterly and entirely different from that of the popular sense. Jung wrote on this most debatable point, "Freud conceives sexuality to be practically synonymous with the word love and to include under this term all those tender feelings and emotions which have had their origin in a primitive erotic source, even if now their primary aim is entirely lost and another substituted for it. It must also be borne in mind that Freud strictly emphasizes the psychic side of sexuality and its importance as well as the somatic expression. Therefore, to understand Freud's theories his very broad conception of the term sexual must never be forgotten."

It is, however, on this very point of sexuality that Jung differs radically from Freud. While Freud postulates that the libido plays a purely sexual rôle, Jung's conception of the libido is that it is particularly concerned with the adaptation of the individual to the environment.

Where, because of weakness of the libido, the individual cannot adequately face reality, retreat from the difficulty of life may take place but Jung considers that the failure of adaptation is due to a present difficulty in the life situation and that the failure of adaptation results in a regression, in a retreat rather than in a fixation, a retreat to an infantile state of development. Jung's view of the libido has points in common with Bergson's *élan vital*. Jung conceives the libido as a fundamental urge and not, as in Freud's view, solely concerned with sexuality.

Again Jung's concept of the unconscious mind differs considerably from that of Freud. Freud conceived the unconscious mind as a reservoir of mental elements and fundamental tendencies which are in conflict with the moral standards of the individual. These tendencies, being incompatible with the personality traits, are repressed and can only be elicited by psychoanalysis. Freud confined unconscious activity to certain conative tendencies, the Freudian wishes.

Jung postulates that while the unconscious contains the personal repressions particular to the individual, it also contains impersonal primordial elements derived from heredity and from the past history of the race. Jung, therefore, recognizes a personal unconscious and a collective unconscious. The concept of the collective unconscious was first postulated by Jung and it explains the origin of many of the strange and bizarre symptoms found in states of dissociation such as in hysteria and schizophrenia.

According to Jung's view the collective unconscious contains archaic material and primordial images, archetypes which are typical of the primitive symbolic and mythological modes of thought characteristic in primitive man. Jung was of the opinion that these fundamental racial strivings and wishes may influence the personality and that their conative value could be utilized when they had been admitted to consciousness under analysis.

It will be seen that Jung differs from Freud in that

Jung's views are collective and racial and do not emphasize the element of sexuality but stress the importance of the adaptation of the individual to present and immediate difficulties of life. Jung holds that regression to the past and retreat to primitive and symbolic modes of mentation occur rather than a fixation at certain levels of mental development. Jung interprets symbolism on the lines of primitive and archaic thought in contradistinction to Freud who uses the terms of sexual symbolism which have been referred to as the language of psychoanalysis. Perhaps, however, the main difference between the two views is that while Freud holds that conflict is essentially concerned with sexuality and attempts to resolve conflict are centred around modes of treating sexuality, Jung emphasizes the importance of the immediate problem of adaptation and the practical and purposive aspect to which mental processes are directed.

The views of Freud and Jung concerning the essential nature of the libido have been indicated in outline and it now remains to consider the concept of the libido formulated by Adler.

ADLER'S INDIVIDUAL PSYCHOLOGY

Adler, who, like Jung, was one of Freud's original supporters, holds that the libido is related only to egoism. The satisfaction of egoism is the terminus of all striving of the libido and it culminates in an attempt to dominate, control and vanquish the environmental conditions.

It has been previously pointed out that during the evolution of the ego the external world has become mentally represented. Concurrently with this process there is a gradual evolution within the ego or concept of the self of those experiences which have particular personal value. This process results in the formation within the constitution of the ego of the unconscious portion of the ego which Freud terms the superego and of an ideal representation of the self or ideal ego. While not fully conscious, the ideal ego strives to overcome whatever deficiencies appear to exist in the ideal contemplation of the self. Here the self attempts to compensate for what may be lacking according to the dictates of the ideal ego. Those attributes which are wanting may be of either a physical or mental character.

It is upon this basis that Adler founded his theory of individual psychology. According to this view all libido striving is a revolt against a mental or physical inferiority. Over-valuation of the ends often results from an excessive development of the ego ideal, a wish for the ego to realize in practice what it has formulated as being in keeping with the ideal representation of the self. Hence the formation of what Adler calls the masculine protest, a mechanism which has its roots within an intrinsic desire to attain to the standards of the social group by which the life situation is largely conditioned.

The fundamental structure of individual psychology is dependent upon the two concepts of the masculine protest and organ inferiority.

The masculine protest is masculine because man has always been regarded as superior and woman as inferior and since striving, according to Adler's view, is basically towards superiority the protest is masculine and is designed to gratify a wish for superiority and to aid in the domination of the life situation. Originating in an inferiority of bodily organs either inherited or acquired and, in this context, Adler includes the mind, the masculine protest is demonstrated by over-functioning of some other organ or by compensatory adaptations being made for underfunctioning.

Organ inferiority according to Adler results in unconscious psychological inferiority which requires mental compensations for the derived inferiority feelings but the tendency is directed towards overcompensation which may eventuate in the evolution of a functional or psychological symptomatology.

Attempts to overcome inferiority frequently result in maladaptations. Should the attempt to dominate the circumstances fail fantasy maintains and supports the frustrated egoistical trends.

Adequate psychological adjustment consists in re-education in social adaptation and in the utilization of the egoistic trends with their inherent libido energies in activities which are in harmony with community standards.

Adler's dynamic concept is clearly related to Schopenhauer's will to live and to Nietzche's will to power. Founded upon the twin concepts of the masculine protest and organ inferiority, Adler restricts compensation to the adjustment of inferiority feelings. The striving to reach the standards laid down by the ego ideal is aided by directive fiction. It is when fiction conflicts with reality that fantasy results as a compromise reaction brought into play for the purpose of maintaining the personal egoistic aims and, in this connection, the tendency is towards placing the burden of nonfulfilment upon environmental conditions rather than upon personal factors. Where compensation is unsuccessful, symptoms of mental disorder may result, the symptoms being, in fact, the inadequate compensations made by the individual.

It must be indicated that the fruition of the conditions established by the ego ideal may be impossible to achieve. The goal of domination may be unattainable and the ideal result may never be reached. Again, Adler disregards the many psychological factors which have contributed in the evolution of the personality before the inferiority is recognized.

Adler's views differ from those of Freud and Jung in the concept of the nature of the libido and in the intrusion of physical factors into psychological theory. It, however, indicates that it is not only the psychological factors that are of importance, adaptation to social conditions and community standards must have its place in the evolution of the well-integrated personality.

CHAPTER XVIII

BEHAVIOURISM AND GESTALT

Two of the main methods of approaching the study of the science of psychology are by introspection and by the study of behaviour.

For many years the introspective method held sway and was postulated as being the most important mode of arriving at the fundamental principles involved in the science. Introspection, however, has its limitations and in the field of the emotions and, particularly in the province of motivation, the introspective method yields but little of value since here introspection becomes retrospection and, as has been shown previously, the unconscious mind has much to do with motivation. Those difficulties, which are inherent in introspection, led to the view that the introspective method required augmenting by the study of behaviour which, in some aspects, may be measured according to the principles involved in the other sciences. From this starting point evolved the concept that the study of behaviour not only threw increasing light upon mental processes but also provided the only means by which the basic principles of psychology could be examined. Stout points out that the observer of his own experience has knowledge which is immediate and direct, but for information concerning the experience of others he is dependent upon language or knowledge of bodily movements gained by external observations and Stout holds that knowledge gained in this way affords only intermediate data.

The more extreme school of behaviourism maintains that the study of behaviour is the science of psychology and the views of Watson, Dunlap, Terman and Thorndike amongst others, have stimulated and elaborated the theoretical importance of behaviour as the only mode of psychological investigation. Dunlap uses the term praxiology to describe behaviour and it is held that psychology is essentially the study of patterns of behaviour. A science, however, grows in knowledge and completeness by using all possible methods of inquiry and while it has been indicated that the introspective method is limited in its application this does not mean that it should be abandoned or that the rôle that consciousness plays in mental life should be disregarded. Introspection must take its place amongst other methods of investigation and while clearly it cannot be the only method employed, its value to the study of psychology is evident, particularly in the understanding of sensation. Knight aptly generalizes when he points out that "the physiological psychologist, the Gestalt psychologist, and the Freudian are not antagonistic; it is simply that they are interested in different aspects of the subject."

From the theoretical point of view behaviourism received an additional impulse from the application of Pavlov's conditioned reflexes to the investigation of psychological processes and the behaviourist school postulates that psychology is the study of behaviour comparable with conditioned and unconditioned reflexes. Here conditioning results from environmental influences and explicit behaviour is the immediate reaction which culminates in behaviour. Implicit behaviour, according to this opinion, is delayed reaction and is made up of internal activities which are not obvious to the observer. The principles of behaviourism are supported by the evidence obtained from child psychology and by the deductions drawn from animal psychology. Behaviourism, however, infers that all human behaviour is the result of conditioned reflexes. In this connection McDougall distinguishes the points at issue between the hormic theory and the tenets of mechanical psychology and summarizes his conclusions in a syllogism "all events are mechanically explicable; the alleged instinctive actions are not mechanically explicable: therefore there is no instinctive action and no instincts." McDougall's opinion is that an open mind should be maintained on such a fundamental question and he draws support from Tolman who admits the inadequacy of mechanistic categories and, although an avowed behaviourist, is of the opinion that the concept of purpose and purposive striving must combat the mechanistic view. The contention of the behaviourist is that instinctive behaviour is nothing more than a train of reflex actions or mechanical responses to physical stimuli, but the added point of ascribing an action or phase of behaviour to a particular instinct enables a forecast to be made regarding the further course of behaviour.

It will be seen that behaviourism is the physiological approach to the study of psychology and that modern views to some extent support this concept but it would appear that behaviourism is not the only answer to the many aspects of mental activity. The rôle that the unconscious mind plays in mental life, the purposive drive which is inherent in instinctive activity and the concept of the self as an arbiter in distinguishing forms of conduct and reaction must also play their part in determining behaviour.

GESTALT PSYCHOLOGY

Thouless describes Gestalt as primarily a research on experimental lines. Its theoretical doctrines have been directed by research and systematized by the results of research. Originated in Wertheimer's exploration of the factors concerned in visual perception the elaboration of the Gestalt theory is primarily the work of Mueller, Lewis, Ogden, Kohler and Koffka.

Gestalt has its origin in Wertheimer's experiments in movement perception and particularly in experiments performed on the appearance of movement which resulted from successive stimulation of two points on the retinal field. Briefly, Wertheimer found that if two points are illuminated successively at certain speeds of succession what is seen is not two bright points in different positions appearing alternately but a single bright point moving between the two positions. The appearance of movement was analogous to that of an actually moving object. This movement could not be explained as a result of movement of the eye since the movement is maintained when the eyes are stationary.

Neither could it be explained by an illusion of judgment. Wertheimer postulated that the movement must be considered to be an experienced effect resulting as immediately from the succession of stimuli as would the experience of a stationary light from the stimulation of any single part of the retina. Helmholtz laid down that every local stimulus in a complex system of stimulation gives rise to its own sensation and that the perception is a psychological resultant of the combination or integration of these sensations. Kohler alludes to this view as the "constancy hypothesis." This hypothesis, however, is not valid when objects are observed as part of a complex perceptual field.

The resultant impression is that in perceptions of objects there are characteristics which do not belong to any sensation. Gestalt, in consequence, denies that the sensations which are apparent as a result of psychological analysis are real constituents of such mental wholes as perceptions. In essence, the Gestalt theory postulates that compounded wholes are the realities and hence sensation and perception cannot be clearly distinguished.

Gestalt means configuration and Kohler has indicated that the real units in the perceptual field are not independent local elements of sensation but are regarded as products of the interaction of different local stimuli with each other. In other words, in the visual field, units have form which is the reason why units are called Gestalten.

According to the Gestalt theory, therefore, perceptual units are determined by the character of the system of units. Thouless points out that a better description of Gestalt psychology would have been the field theory of psychology since the essential theory of perception is that it regards all perceptions as occurring in a perceptual field of which the properties of the whole are determined by the properties of the field. It will be seen that much of the work of the Gestalt school has been concerned with the study of perception although at the same time the psychological problems of insight, learning and memory are explainable on Gestalt theorization.

To summarize, Gestalt postulates that mental phenomena

must be studied in wholes and not in component parts. In perception what is perceived cannot be explained by the aggregation of numerous sensations. Something must be added that is characteristic of the wholeness of the sensation. Parts may be grouped in "sets" and "forms" may be evolved perceived in terms of "wholes." Gestalt psychology endeavours to demonstrate that there is a mental capacity to perceive in whole and that in cognition the wholeness of the situation is a predominating factor.

It will be seen that in the theory of Gestalt an organized sense-field which is dependent upon cerebral process is fundamental. It may be that the cerebral association areas are implicated in assembling parts into wholes. This process of grouping together elements of the sense-field seems to be influenced by the qualities of similarity, symmetry proximity, continuity and completeness.

There seems but little doubt that this tendency to organize the sense-field is innate and not learned by experience. Gestalt psychology maintains that the awareness of pattern or structure within the sense-field is natively determined. While the processes of recognition and identification must be learnt by experience the result of impressions upon an organized sense-field is a Gestalt and not independent local elements of sensation. Hence an entity is not only composed of its parts, there is the added factor of the relationships between the parts which Gestalt postulates as being apprehended innately and simultaneously. This view is in opposition to previous psychological theorization which held that the apprehension of relationships followed the apprehension of the qualities of the parts. As Knight points out, "every Gestalt has qualities that are not possessed by its elements and about which we can learn nothing by studying its elements separately."

Insight, the process of obtaining knowledge principally regarding relationships accelerates the process of learning. Basically, insight is observation of some fact or observation of the relationship between facts. Gestalt psychology throws some light upon the essential processes involved in insight. Insight is developed by the amalgamation of separate parts into a cohesive whole or Gestalt by integration of new facts and, by structurization, the appreciation of structure within an apparently unsystematized confusion. Its characteristic here lies in the reorganization of the perceptual field.

Physiologically considered insight, according to the Gestalt theory is conditioned by what are called patterns of excitation in the neurological structure of the cortex. This theory of the isomorphism of cerebral processes and of perception is speculative and dependent upon the pattern or related system of stimulation of the association areas which may be conditioned by the relationships or differences in electric potential (Lashley).

SECTION II

PSYCHOLOGY AND PSYCHIATRY

CHAPTER I

GENERAL PRINCIPLES

Psychology may be defined as the science which classifies and analyses the phenomena or varying states of the mind. Under this definition psychiatry might be included since mental disorder is, in essence, a variation of what is conceived as normal. Psychiatry, however, is a term that has been restricted to the treatment of mental disorder. It is obvious that the differentiation is more of degree than of kind and is dependent upon the meaning of the word normal. Here again it must be emphasized that perhaps of all the sciences psychology is most related to exact terminology. Hence the importance of arriving at correct definitions. The word normal implies the establishment of an exact and authoritative standard of judgment and it is here that psychiatry differs from psychology.

Whereas the science of psychology consists of the observation and recording of mental phenomena and the classification of the recorded phenomena into series and divisions, the practical implication is that of utility and explanation of the facts discovered which may be used in a prediction of the occurrence of future facts. Hence psychiatry must be guided by the same scientific criteria if it is to take its place as a science seeking to explain the various phenomena of the disordered mind. The difficulty here is that conceptions are used that cannot be proved to have any actual phenomenal existence. Such factors as complexes and repressions are conceptions elaborated to explain observed phenomena. The existence of unconscious mental processes assume that mental processes exist concerning which the individual has no cognizance. Theoretically, these conceptions may be justified since they explain in some measure the facts of experience.

The assessment of normality, however, is a difficult problem since concepts of normality differ from epoch to epoch and are predominantly conditioned by the concepts ruling at the time. The concepts of insanity and sanity are dependent upon the state of knowledge at the time of their formulation and when, with changing concepts, criteria require alterations these changes are reflected in the general opinion and in new classifications of knowledge. For these reasons a more practical basis for distinguishing the deviations from so-called normality is required and, hence, mental disorder has tended to become assessed upon conduct and behaviour as in Mercier's definition of mental disorder as a disorder of conduct and in Devine's postulate that mental disorder was a disorder of behaviour at the social or conscious level. Here the implications are that sound mentality is synonymous with the well-integrated mind, a mind that may be described as adapted to the environment and which has been able to deal successfully with its repressions and whose rationalizations are less evident and more acceptable than those of a postulated disordered mind.

It will be seen that all psychological processes finally issue in conduct and therefore behaviour has become a criterion of mind and while mental good health is indicated by the conduct which is appropriate and in line with the ruling circumstances, mental ill health is typified externally by disorders of behaviour and conduct which reflect the mentality sequence at the time of their operation.

The factors in the establishment and conservation of the well-integrated personality are those of innate constitution and, particularly those which are dependent upon the capacity for adaptation. In this context the mechanisms of repression and sublimation must be unimpaired especially in connection with the instinctive urges. Reinforced by example and precept, directed by education and training, refined by contact with community standards and predominantly evolved by parental suggestion and childhood circumstances, mentality evolves within the well-integrated personality and results in that comprehensive contact with the environmental conditions which is imperative in the growth of the organized personality.

While the influence of heredity and of genetic factors are of primary importance in the development of the individual, the rôle played by environment and social influences cannot be neglected. Here McDougall's concept of primitive passive sympathy is involved, a tendency which characterizes all gregarious animals. Sympathy of this primitive character is, in McDougall's view, the cement that stabilizes community life and influences the harmonious relationships of group society while, at the same time, allowing the personality to enjoy the benefits of social organization in spite of lack of intelligence. Connected with primitive passive sympathy which essentially means a feeling with, is empathy, a feeling into, a projection of the personality into the object observed and obtaining the satisfaction of the onlooker who, in imagination, is conceived to be the object of perception. Here the basic motive is one of power and domination and forms an outlet for the self-assertive impulse.

Mental disorder, however, is more than the general changes which have been indicated. Psychologically considered there is a diminution involving all the capacities of the mind. Mentation, cognition, action, memory and affect may be impaired to a varying degree.

It has been previously indicated, however, that psychology must automatically consider to some extent the physiological processes that accompany psychological phenomena and in the same way psychiatry must take into account not only the psychological aspects but also physiological factors which may be concomitant. Psychosomatic disorders in which mental factors condition physical disorders as in functional cardiac disturbances and in some cases of gastric and duodenal ulcer emphasize the interdependence of psychological and physiological processes and illustrate the two main concepts ruling in psychiatry, the physiological concept which stresses the dependence of mental processes upon neurological and cerebral changes and the psychological concept which regards the conscious processes displayed in mental disorder as the actual phenomena with which psychiatry is concerned. Hence the theories of interaction and psycho-physical parallelism are implicated. The ultimate discussion of these points lies in the realm of philosophy.

Psychiatry, however, is concerned with the accurate assessment of the psychological and physiological factors involved in the causation of mental disorder, in the evolution and explanation of its symptomatology and particularly in the formulation of methods of treatment. Due consideration must be given to the two principal factors implicated if the test of utility, which is the only true criteria of science, is to be adequately fulfilled.

It is therefore essential to relate any working hypothesis to the individual case but there are certain standards of knowledge which, in their application to psychiatry, afford assistance and of these, from the psychological viewpoint, the concepts of mind, purpose and instinct are of importance.

It would appear clear that the mind has been evolved in order to control and appreciate the environment. The sensational aspect of mind augmented by inherited or acquired mental dispositions conveys to the mind a meaning which conditions and influences behaviour. The working of consciousness involves choice of reaction to sensory stimulation which choice demonstrates the unity of the mind by the awareness of purpose. To achieve purpose action is necessary and action implies mental or vital energy. It has already been indicated that the nature of this vital energy is debatable and its essential characteristics vary according to the view held. The libidos of Freud and Jung, the concepts of Bergson and McDougall, amongst others, differ in detail but not markedly so in principle. The conception of the unconscious mind has revolutionized the study of mental disorder particularly on the subjects of motivation, psychological mechanisms and personality. To the consideration of these factors must be added the crucial factor the problem of adaptation.

Mind in its primary function of understanding and controlling the environment is frequently confronted by situations concerning which neither proper understanding nor control can be exercised. Faced by conditions of this type the necessity for adaptation becomes paramount. In addition, adaptation to inner personal trends which because of the life situation and because of the personality traits cannot obtain adequate satisfaction is continually necessary. The capacity for adaptation is, therefore, an essential feature of mental life and by its help psychological unity, integrity and harmonious relations with environmental factors are achieved. Where there is serious failure of adaptation a varying degree of psychological disorganization becomes inevitable and may result in psychoneurotic or psychotic symptom-formation. Should lack of adaptation be principally concerned with environmental conditions modifications may possibly be made in the situation circumstances and sometimes the individual is unconsciously directed towards ways of life that may be within the range of the adaptative powers, but where environmental stresses become superimposed upon inadequacy of adaptation, mental disorder is apt to occur, the maladaptations which are made by the personality being displayed in the symptomatology.

It will be seen that the origination of many forms of mental disorder lies in maladaptations of the personality to environmental conditions and to unconscious impulses. But the type of reaction displayed varies with the character trends of the individual who must be regarded as a psychobiological organism with an individual reaction to the environment. According to this view, therefore, mental disorder is a personality disorder resulting from the maladjustments of constitutional types to the environment and from the personal adjustments made to impulses arising within the deeper layers of the mind. It is manifest that there is no single cause conditioning the genesis of mental disorders, rather there is a complex of etiological factors, varying in relative strength and intensity, arising from obscure beginnings, influenced by internal and external circumstances, by hereditary handicaps, and by the distorted emergence into consciousness of unconscious tendencies. It is in the summation of these factors and the mode of individual reaction to them that the deviation from normality which is manifested in the strange and bizarre symptoms of mental illness originates. Hence all mental illnesses are personality disorders, types of individual reaction. Their symptoms are, in fact, the mode of reaction of the individual patient. The symptoms of mental disorder indicate the abnormal psychological processes that are in operation and the accurate valuation of the symptomatology reinforced by the proper assessment of the circumstances of the life history and of the environmental conditions supplies the diagnosis. Modern views on psychopathology emphasize the rôle played by the unconscious mind in the production of symptoms of mental disorder. Where unharmonious unconscious tendencies emerge into consciousness symptom production follows and at times consciousness may be overwhelmed by the emergence of unconscious material.

It is, however, convenient to consider the general principles involved in the disordered mind under the categories of quantitative and qualitative. Hart has pointed out that quantitative qualities are displayed in mental defectiveness and in dementia. In mental deficiency there is a lack of general mental capacity which is displayed in all the attributes of mind. Mentation, action, memory and particularly intelligence are seriously impaired. In mental defect this impairment is due to congenital causes which result in the inadequate development of the normal mental equipment. Lack of development may show itself in a great variety of degree which is reflected in the legal definitions of mental defectiveness and in the categories of idiocy, imbecility and feeblemindedness. The grades of mental defectiveness range between entire lack of adaptation to the environment where the individual requires constant supervision and attention to a partial but not complete adaptation which necessitates care, supervision and control. Whereas mental deficiency arises from congenital causes, dementia is conditioned by acquired causes of which the predominating casual factor is age. Decay of the normal mental equipment results in the abrogation of intelligence, as Aristophanes wrote, "Old age is but a second childhood." In some cases, however, senility is not the principal factor involved and the presenile dementias illustrate the dependence of psychological processes upon cerebral changes.

Where mental disorder is actuated by qualitative changes these are reflected in the general attitude of mind regarding affect. Excitement, depression and apathy are prominent symptoms displayed in a majority of mental cases. Excitement implies a pouring out of the affect attached to the libido or vital energy which has been seen to be the source of action. Increased excitement and depression characterizes the manic-depressive psychosis and these affects are accompanied by acceleration or retardation of mental and physical manifestations which show no relationship to the environmental conditions. Distractabiity of attention is usually marked in the excited phase and lack of attention typifies the depressive syndrome. These symptoms are diametrically opposed to the apathy which is so characteristic of some forms of schizophrenia. Affect here is conditioned by interest and desire and where these conative impulses are in abeyance there is want of emotional response and consequent indifference to the exigencies of life.

These mental manifestations, because of their strangeness and their lack of unity with normal conscious processes, seem as if they are evolved from a different personality whose mental processes run concurrently but uniquely separate from the basic personality traits of the individual. They, however, are the product of dissociation which Freud has demonstrated to result from unresolved conflict.

Mental dissociation to some degree exists in the normal individual. While usually the momentary field of consciousness is uniform, containing sensations, ideas and volitions directed and connected by some common aim, consciousness may be occupied by two different processes existing within the sense-field of consciousness as in typing, where the process of attending to the typewriter occupies part of the same field of consciousness as is occupied by attention to the material typed. Here, however, the dissociation of consciousness is only temporary and is under the control of the will. While normally the self may expand in several directions and two or more selves may be present in the same organism the manifestation of the various selves does not cause marked alteration in conduct since the individual is well integrated and his various selves are so co-ordinated as to harmonize well together.

In the dissociation which is a causative factor in the symptomatology of mental disorder, however, the mind is divided into independent fragments which are not co-ordinated together to attain some common end. This lack of integration results in a division of the mind into compartments, each compartment being dissociated from the other and carrying on its own mental processes independent of the control of the whole personality.

Pathological dissociation is characteristically seen in hysteria, somnambulism, automatic writing and in delusions and hallucinations. In cases of double personality the stream of consciousness is divided into two and a primary and secondary personality may be evolved, each pursuing its own course independently. In these cases there may be some alteration in the experiences connected with organic sensation. In obsessional cases dissociation is present but here the patient is aware of the dissociated system which is sometimes likened to some external force which cannot be controlled by the personality.

A somewhat analogous phenomenon is seen in a fixed idea. Here consciousness is dominated by the idea of the action and volition is not in operation resulting in removal of restraint and a disruption of the harmony and unity of the self. Here the impulse of conation is in abeyance and deliberation leading to judgment does not take place.

It will be seen that dissociation is an integral factor in the psychological production of mental symptoms. Normally, unconscious factors co-operate harmoniously and facilitate conscious reaction. In mental illness unconscious factors which are in disharmony with the conscious life may obtain satisfaction by symbolization, emerging into consciousness in a symbolical form, or by invading consciousness and swamping normal conscious life. It is clear that these unconscious factors are activitated independently of consciousness and, being unconnected with conscious processes, operate as dissociated systems.

Mental dissociation is a process conditioned by the two factors of repression and lack of appreciation of connection. It has been seen that repression originates from conflict of the repressed material with the ego ideal. It is, however, not so much the repressed material that is manifest in symptomatology as the accompanying affect which frequently takes the form of conscious anxiety. In the same way, inadequate recognition of emotional connections lead to emotion being displaced (displacement of affect) from one topic or situation to another. Emotion or affect must have attachments in consciousness and, where these are not normally and correctly supplied, affect may become attached to entirely unrelated ideas in comparison with the original affective circumstance. This displacement of affect is well seen in the genesis of anxiety states, compulsive and obsessional ideas and is the process by which unrelated ideas and impulses become substituted for the original idea with which affect was predominantly associated. Hence the growth of anxiety and fears concerning extraneous and totally unrelated factors. The patient, who is unaware of this tendency of affect to obtain attachment, displays symptoms of psychological disorder mostly concerned with anxiety and vague fears which culminate in a psychoneurosis. Affect, however, attains its full strength particularly when instinctive impulses are thwarted and are unable to obtain gratification. Impediments to the adequate functioning of the instincts may result in repression not only of the vital energy (libido) inherent in instinctive activity but also of the powerful emotional trends that accompany the evocation of instinctive reaction. This process results in complex formation and where antagonistic complexes clash the ensuing conflict is charged with strong emotional tone. It will be seen that one of the primary factors in the causation of the psychoses is not only the presence in the mind of unconscious and fragmentated mental activity but also of the affect inherent within the conflict which dissipates itself in the affective symptoms of mental disorder.

Unconscious factors, however, are not the only qualities involved in the production of mental symptoms. It has been pointed out that the primary function of mind is to control the environment and where environmental stresses are beyond the individual's capacity for control they form a fruitful source of precipitating factors in mental illness. Mental stresses may arise from a great variety of difficulties which are inherent in the life situation. Thwarted ambitions, difficulties in adjustment to changed circumstances, financial worries and responsibilities, the comparison of the present with the past, the sorrows of death and the impingement of age, all require active and co-ordinated powers of adaptation and adjustment. These situations are charged with a high emotional potential and it is this rather than the actual circumstances that precipitates mental breakdown. Again, physical illness and mental shock leads to a failure of repression while prolonged worry and anxiety with their affective concomitants may result in fatigue, exhaustion and lack of power in the repressive processes with an ensuing appearance of psychological symptoms.

It must be emphasized that mental disorder is a disorder of mental function. Physical illness and bodily disease have their place within the scale of causative factors but in the great majority of mental illnesses mental factors, unassociated with physical changes, are of primary importance in the genesis of mental disorder.

CHAPTER II

MENTAL MECHANISMS

It has been seen that the psychogenic theory of the causation of mental disorder is that mental illness is due to intrapsychic conflict. Freud considered that the conflict was always of a sexual character, using the word sexual in the Freudian sense. Jung, on the other hand, was of the opinion that the conflict arose from present difficulties. Mental conflict, however, is general throughout life and cannot be avoided.

The well-integrated mind is able to resolve its conflicts sufficiently adequately to escape symptom production of the more serious type. The normal method of solving conflict is by sublimation or directing the energy and affect attached to the conflict into other channels and thus obtain a substitute gratification. It has been seen that repression is another method of dealing with conflict but this mode is unsatisfactory because of displacement of affect. Self-control or suppression of antagonistic impulses is a further mode of dealing with conflict. Here, however, the process is conscious and choice, deliberation and judgment are involved. Essentially, self-control is determined by the unity of the self, by the harmonious working of all the faculties of the mind. Self-control is supported by ideals, by the organization of the sentiments and by the evolution of moral principles. Failure of self-control results from lack of the proper evolution of the concept of the self and of the development of self-consciousness. Where organic conditions operate towards disorganization of the self lack of self-control is seen in conduct as in senile dementia.

Sublimation and repression are modes of escape in conflict and of avoiding its attached affective tone. They were named by Freud, mental mechanisms, and to these mechanisms must be added the mechanisms of rationalization, projection, symbolization, defence, fantasy, identification, compensation, comprise and substitution.

The mechanism of rationalization allows the mind to accept facts connected with complexes and delusional schemes providing that the distortion supplied by rationalization is present. In general, motives for actions and beliefs are obscure and it is not often that the correct motive is assigned to the resultant action or belief. On inquiry into the motive for a belief or action there is a tendency to seek a rational explanation for the action or belief. This explanation appears reasonable and motives for beliefs and actions are usually explained according to the principle of sufficient reason. Very frequently, however, the motive operating is entirely different and even repugnant to personal consciousness. Sometimes an explanation is invented and produced as a so-called true motive. The essential point in rationalization is that rationalization seeks to justify actions and beliefs according to logical rather than to emotional reasons. Psychologically, a rearrangement of the situation takes place and a preformed judgment is passed and consideration is only given to those facts which can be arranged to lead logically to the preformed judgment. By this means conflict is avoided and motives that are out of harmony with the personality are distorted and changed by the evolution of invented explanations that replace the true motive. Hence rationalization is a mechanism that justifies actions and beliefs by pseudological reasoning rather than by emotional reasons. There is a relationship between long continued and persistent moods and rationalization. Pathological moods seek suitable objects and may create objects in the form of delusions and hallucinations. In normal psychological processes rationalization is ever present since we believe what we wish to believe and do not commonly wish to attribute our actions and beliefs to their true motivation.

Projection, a mental mechanism which is seen preeminently in paranoia, has two meanings. Normally, in alluding to the perceptual image, it is described as projecting away from the organism. The object is not perceived in the eye or in the cortex but it seems to be in the distance where it is actually situated. In psychopathology, however, the mechanism of projection indicates the tendency to interpret the behaviour of others by the motives that actuate our own conduct. Ultimate motives for conduct are always obscure and conduct in others is usually assumed to be conditioned by the same motives that would dominate ourselves in the same circumstances. While this inference is frequently unjustified it remains the only possible means of understanding the motives of others. It follows that the individual projects his own motives into other persons in order to explain their conduct. Where there is some peculiarity of personality trait in one's own personality, there is the probability that one's opinions of others is strongly influenced by it and therefore a distorted view of others results.

Where the mind is disturbed by complexes which are at variance with the personality it may react to a repressed complex by regarding it as being produced by the outer world. Here the contents of the complex are projected on to some other imaginary or real person. By this means the contents of the complex become conscious but conflict is avoided by treating the complex as not belonging to the individual but as being a part of external reality. To some degree, projection is a defence mechanism which frequently gives rise to the mental symptoms of persecutory delusions and ideas of reference. In persecutory delusions, the repressed material obtains indirect expression by projection. In ideas of reference, a mental state in which the individual is suspicious and paranoid and hence believes that external happenings have a special reference to himself, projection supplies a mode of avoiding conflict since the affect attached to the complex is projected. Usually the mechanism of projection is concerned with guilt feelings which are projected on to others. Psychopathologically, the mechanism of projection is found in the so-called paranoid forms of schizophrenia, in paraphrenia and particularly in paranoia in which Freud postulates that, owing to the failure of repression and sublimation, the evolution of the consequent characteristic delusional system exhibited in this psychosis is dependent on projection.

Symbolization is a further psychological mechanism and is an important factor in mental life and its influence is apparent throughout all human activity. Symbolization is the tendency to value objects of thought or perception beyond their intrinsic worth. Primarily, the power of symbolization is inherent in the fact that the symbolical or object-idea is capable of arousing emotions that deflect the conative tendencies far more than the perceptual experiences warrant. Objects that have been perceived at the time of experiencing some strong affective disturbance tend to become associated with that particular emotion and may become symbols with the power of reactivating that emotion. The practical issue in symbolism is that the symptoms of mental disorder may be symbolical of the unresolved conflict. Symbolism is particularly prominent in mythology, folklore and dreams and the principle of symbolization is used extensively in the technique of psychoanalysis. In dreams, the repressed wishes evade the vigilance of the superego by expression in symbolic form. To some extent there is an identical and universal meaning for many classes of symbols which may be interpreted in the same way.

Defence mechanisms are seen in organic disorder and in the reaction of the tissues to invading bacteria. Here physical defence results from the effects of infection. Psychologically, however, defence mechanisms are well illustrated during the operation of the instincts of escape and of self-preservation. Should there be alterations in the fundamental sentiments of the personality there is often deprivation of logical control of the situation. In psychical conditions of this nature the development of defence mechanisms such as phantasy production and the mechanism of projection, combat mental pain and distress. Here the failure to react to the situation and its difficulties is offset, not by the logical conscious method of the normal individual but by the evolution of psychological defences which ensue in conduct changes and influence mental processes. When the emotional stress that has produced the sensation has subsided the subject reverts to his normal psychological state and the defence mechanism is no longer needed.

The psychological mechanisms of phantasy and identification are mental mechanisms that release the tension of complexes by imaginary fulfilment, by autistic thought, of the complex content. Hence fantasy or day-dreaming is a mode of satisfying complexes. Here there is a retreat from reality into a self-created world where all wishes are satisfied and difficulties do not exist. Phantasy or autistic thought is compared to realistic or adapted thought. While in the realistic type of thought each association is aroused and controlled by some interest and by some conative urge, autistic thought or phantasy thinking is conditioned by desire and not by reality. While normal thought processes are difficult and demand sustained effort and attention, autistic thought is devoid of criticism, effort and the pursuit of a goal idea. Phantasy and autistic thinking are methods of retirement from mundane circumstances and of ignoring the unpleasant realities of community life by retreating from a world which constantly demands efforts in adaptation and in attention. Phantasy, however, serves a useful purpose in planning for the future. Here a connection with reality is preserved and dissociation is only partial and temporary. In psychopathology, however, phantasy is a defence mechanism and dissociation may be complete and permanent. In schizophrenia, phantasy may usurp the totality of mental content which becomes entirely divorced from reality. In phantasy the mind constructs its own images. In identification the person views himself as another or fictitious person which may become amalgamated within the personality. This secondary personality with its desires and emotions is, as in the manifestations of hysteria, considered to be incorporated within the primary personality. Hence delusional schemes may arise in identification and fragmentation of the personality may become evident. Identification according to McDougall has points in common with imitation and, according to this view, may be regarded as unconscious imitation.

The mental mechanism of compensation comes into play when sublimation fails. Where sublimation is inadequate a state of psychological inferiority may ensue and then the mind unconsciously compensates for its pyschical disability by excessive development of some other attribute of the personality. There is a tendency for compensation to become excessive and overcompensation may result in symptoms of psychoneurotic or psychotic mental disorder. Overcompensation is a principal factor in Adler's theory of the causation of mental illness where the defect in one attribute of the personality is compensated by the over-development of some other personality character. The process of compensation is also shown in physical disorders as in myocardial insufficiency in its relation to the growth of cardiac muscle fibre.

Compromise and substitution are two mental mechanisms which may be shown when sublimation is ineffective. In compromise the results of intrapsychic conflict is symbolized in the symptoms of mental disorder and the repressed wish is expressed by conversion into the symptom as in conversion hysteria. In substitution it is the affect, which is in relationship to the repressed wish, that is concerned and which, by the mechanism of substitution, becomes attached to some other idea which may symbolize the intolerable idea which has been repressed. The process of substitution may eventuate into an obsessional-compulsive state in which the obsession or compulsive act symbolizes in a disguised form the wish which has been repressed and which is out of harmony with the conscious personality.

The variety and number of these mental mechanisms emphasize the strength and pertinacity of the energy and affective continuity of unconscious processes. They illustrate the inherent and fundamental striving for expression, satisfaction and gratification of the contents of the unconscious mind. From the practical aspect, however, mental mechanisms are indicators and keys to the understanding of the symptomatology of mental illness. As guides to psychological treatment their value is considerable, as adjuvants to the elucidation of the psychological aspects of mental disorder they form concepts which are of the highest importance. Intrinsically, mental mechanisms throw light upon the essential character of mental disorder and upon the predominating rôle played by psychology in psychiatry since the psychological state of patients suffering from mental disorder results in many cases from the operation of psychological defences. The crucial factor here is that a disease process is not operating but that the patient is simply displaying a failure to overcome the particular situation involved. The signs of failure are the symptoms displayed but the symptoms are, in fact, the psychological reactions of the mind towards the situation, defence processes evoked to assist the mind in its mental emergency. These factors have to be considered in treatment and attempts at psychological treatment may defeat their object since they may tend only to increase the defensive mechanism. Hence the importance of the time factor in mental illness. Time allows the affective attributes of mental processes to withdraw and become dissipated to an extent that they cease to fully occupy mentation and are no longer principal factors in the conditioning of behaviour.

CHAPTER III

DELUSION, HALLUCINATION, ILLUSION

It has previously been seen that the evolution of belief is dependent upon a variety of factors. Sensational experiences result in perceptional inferences, further sensational experiences may contradict the primary perceptional inference. While perception simplifies sensory experience, ideation aggregates the results of general experience. An ideational inference which is conditioned by experience of reality is like a perception and is accepted by the conscious mind and therefore is believed. True belief must correspond with reality and must be able to pass the test of experience but, as beliefs vary from epoch to epoch and are primarily governed by the beliefs in general use at the time and are also influenced by educational and environmental conditions, the essential differences between true and false beliefs is a topic that cannot be accurately determined because of the varying standards of belief. Hence it will be seen that the estimation of the truth and falsity of belief is conditioned by a number of unrelated factors and that, in general, to express an opinion as to the falsity of beliefs may be a difficult task.

Persistent false beliefs that remain uncorrected by the facts of experience and the percepts of logic are termed delusions but care must be taken before a belief is stigmatized as a delusion. The practical aspect, however, requires consideration since belief determines conduct and, as it has been seen, behaviour is a criterion of mind. Here again psychological principles are estimated by their results and in mental disorder it is the resultant behaviour which is in reality the test of the truth or falsity of belief. Psychologically a delusion is a persistent false belief and a manifestation of inadequacy of judgment, but persistent false beliefs may be normal or abnormal. The rôle played by delusions in psychological disorder is apt to be overstressed particularly in the legal aspect of mental illness which, perhaps, placed too much insistence upon the presence or absence of delusions. It must be emphasized that a person may be legally insane without displaying any mental delusional content.

Devine pointed out that it is better to renounce any attempt to define delusion since the term may convey a variety of meanings and its validity is intrinsically dependent upon the mentality and judgment of the observer. Some guide, however, may be given regarding the essential differences between normal false beliefs and pathological delusions. In the normal false beliefs these are usually evolved from the environmental conditions of the individual. They are collective beliefs held by the community in which the person has his being. Examples of this class are found in the beliefs of primitive races and of un-civilized communities. Here the system of beliefs forms part of the individual's social heritage and hence have the attributes of familiarity and reality. Again, normal false beliefs are expressed in language that is readily understood and they contain concepts which are familiar and akin to those of the normal mind. Even at the present time there are many people who believe that the world is flat, that numerology influences conduct or that the future can be foretold by regarding tea-leaves in a cup. These are normal false beliefs held by a minority. A fundamental characteristic of belief which is found in the highly evolved and educated mind is the isolated and mutually unsupporting systems of beliefs that may exist in a highly developed mind. Hence the importance of deriving beliefs from rational sources and not from the prestige of those who may have distinguished themselves in one branch of knowledge only.

On considering pathological false beliefs or true delusions it is manifest that these proceed from the individual psyche and are not conditioned by external circumstances. The delusion is an individual belief not shared by others of the same educational and social status and is peculiar and particular to the person. A halo of strangeness and unreality surrounds the delusion whose content is frequently expressed in incomprehensible and bizarre conduct. The true delusion contains concepts that are completely alien to the normal mentality and is surrounded by an atmosphere of unreality and strangeness which is indicative of its unconscious motivation.

From the practical viewpoint a delusion is not true in fact and cannot be corrected by an appeal to reason or experience. Further, it is out of harmony with the individual's social setting and mental capacity and it is essentially founded on ideas which do not logically or reasonably result in the conclusions reached.

During the development of a delusion the individual experiences a sense of discomfort, tension, restlessness or vague persecution. Following this stage, delusional images emerge which symbolize the nature of the stimulus of which they are the conscious expression. On full fruition of the delusion there is cessation of tension and a feeling tone of tranquillity and certainty.

It will be seen that delusions arise from inadequately repressed complexes which find expression of the conflicting trends in a distorted form in the delusion. Further, delusions frequently arise in connection with the mechanism of projection where the contents of complexes are projected on to some imaginary or actual person. In communicational mental disorder or *folie à deux*, delusions may be communicated to someone, often the husband, wife or sister, who is in constant association with the deluded person.

There are a variety of classifications of delusions but classification itself throws but little light upon causation. Perhaps the most useful form of classification is that which ranks delusions under the headings of the fixed delusion, the changeable delusions, the systematized delusions and the unsystematized delusions. Fixed delusions are those which are permanent and unchangeable and which become incorporated into the individual's personality. In changeable delusions there is a continual shifting delusional state as in the delusions displayed in mania. Systematized delusions are typical of paranoia. Here the delusional scheme is associated with other facts of conscious experience and the delusional system motivates conduct. Systematized delusions are supported by pseudological reasoning and argument, they appeal to experience and often form the basis of the personality. In unsystematized delusions, organization of the delusional scheme is lacking and the delusions are unrelated to other conscious facts. Unsystematized delusions rarely seriously affect conduct but they are entirely divorced from reality, argument and logic.

The varieties of delusions are protean but four main categories may be differentiated. Delusions of grandeur, which are often compensatory in nature, particularly when the self-assertive impulse is impeded, are found in mania, paranoia, paraphrenia and dementia paralytica. Delusions of sin and persecution may originate in repressed homosexuality and in the melancholic phase of manic-depressive psychosis and in involutional melancholia. Delusions of negation are of some psychological importance. These nihilistic delusions, where the patient believes that he no longer exists or that the whole world is destroyed are typically found in involutional melancholia and, at times, in schizophrenia. Their development originates in a clouding of consciousness which passes into a state of anxiety and confusion resulting in unreality feelings and changes in the appreciation of external reality, these changes being due to lack of integration of the self. Delusions of negation express in a disguised form the alterations in the patient's concept and affect of reality and they symbolize the mysterious, terrifying and unaccountable alterations in the appreciation of the environment. Hypochondriacal delusions are particularly common in involutional melancholia and are found in organic conditions in which organic changes are reflected in mental life.

The psychological interpretation of delusions is subject to the various views on the essential causative factors involved in mental disorder. The psychoanalytic school hold that delusions are wish fulfilments which are displayed in a disguised form. The delusion here is a substitute for the unrealized wish or a compromise between the dictates of the superego and the desires of the unconscious mind. The evolution of delusions according to this view is conditioned by defence reactions, compensations and projections. Here the patient lives in a world of his own divorced from the reality principle and his delusions typify the striving of complexes for expression. Jung has pointed out that in the deteriorating schizophrenic the delusional content shows those archaic features typical of the deep unconscious and comparable with the racial and primitive modes of thought. McDougall emphasizes in his delusions of desire and aversion the influence of fear and volition since we believe what we wish to believe and predominantly one believes what one fears. On the other hand, Devine postulated that delusions are symbolical of organic disturbance. Changes in the vegetative aspects of the organism are symbolized in delusions and the individual reality of delusions are, in fact, the reality of organic change the delusion being the symbol in consciousness of organic change.

The practical factor in delusion, however, is the psychological factor, the factor of judgment. While judgment in the normal individual is to some extent conditioned by a logical acceptance of the facts, it is clear that judgment is much influenced by affect. Where affect plays a disproportionate part in the passing of judgment as is often the case, faulty judgment results and, in the predisposed individual, delusions make their appearance.

On considering the evolution and attributes of hallucinations the problem is not so complicated. A hallucination is a perception without sensory foundation in the environment. Where there may be a physiological or pathological process occurring in the sensory end-organs the resultant is strictly an illusion and not a hallucination. Hallucinations have been defined as perceptions without any actual objective stimulus. Here an image is taken for a sensation, a recalled fact is mistaken for a present objective fact. Strictly, hallucinations are percepts experienced in the absence of any peripheral stimulus. Hallucinations have all the attributes of perception and, essentially, the only difference is in the mode of origin. While perceptions are conditioned externally, hallucinations result from internal causation. Hallucinations have the vividness and qualities of real experience and, consequently, in their results affect the organism in the same way with resulting influence upon behaviour. While all hallucinations are sensory responses aroused by substitute stimuli, the point at issue is that the subject of hallucinatory experiences is not aware of the method of their origin.

James has pointed out that hallucinations may occur in normal individuals as in auditory hallucinations resulting from local disorder of the auditory system. Strictly, however, here there is some admixture of illusion. The difference between hallucination and illusion lies in the fact that illusion is conditioned by misinterpretation of the external stimulus while a hallucination occurs without any external stimulus.

In hallucination the subject's dependence on objective circumstances is influenced by his desires and fears and his hallucinatory content is in line with his desires and fears. Like delusions, hallucinations involve faulty reasoning and judgment.

Hallucinations are important symptoms in mental illness since an hallucinated patient is very prone to act upon the apparent reality of an hallucinatory experience. The seeing of visions, and the constant hearing of imaginary voices frequently give rise to outbursts of sudden or premeditated violence as in schizophrenia and paranoia.

Psychologically, hallucinations are conditioned by unconscious factors. Repressed material obtains entry into the conscious mind in a disguised form but since the material is incompatible with the ego the disguised wish must come from the environment. By the mechanism of projection the disguised wish assumes an external sensory appearance as an hallucination.

There is a relationship between hallucinations and dreams. In dreams the objective situation is lost sight of and images appear as real. In hypnogogic hallucinations, those hallucinations which appear between sleeping and waking, the images appear very real and are taken to be actual sensations. Hallucinations may be conditioned by drugs such as opium and its derivatives and by mescal, which, because of its stimulant action upon the visual and visuo-psychic areas of the cortex, produces a great variety of visual hallucinations. Synaesthesia, excitation of one sense organ evoking a train of phenomena pertaining to another sense organ, is also prominent in mescalism. Alcohol and carbon dioxide narcosis also produce hallucinatory experiences.

In mental disorder there are several varieties of hallucination encountered of which probably the most common is the auditory. Auditory hallucinations are of all kinds ranging from simple sounds like the ringing of bells to the hearing of voices. The voices are usually located externally but may be located as coming from different parts of the body as in the epigastric voice. Visual hallucinations occur in all grades from simple flashes of light or colour to complete and complex visions. Lilliputian or microptic hallucinations may be symptoms of mescalism and alcoholism and are also sometimes found in typhoid and scarlet fever. Hallucinations of taste and smell may occur in melancholia and paraphrenia but are particularly concerned with a physiogenic causation in tumours of the uncus. Haptic hallucinations are hallucinations of touch, pain, heat and cold and may occur in cocaine addiction, alcoholism and in paraphrenia.

Illusion requires further distinguishing from hallucination. An illusion is a false perception, a perception which has been aroused by some stimulus that is wrongly interpreted. The stimulus results in an act of perception but the mind reads the wrong meaning into it. It has been seen that according to the psychic-stimulus theory the ultimate meaning of a perception is supplied by the mind reacting to a clue given by the senses. In illusion the mind supplies the wrong meaning. Any condition of expectant attention is particularly liable to originate illusions. A further factor in illusion is that of the emotional state present at the time.

This factor is well demonstrated by the instinct of escape in which the powerful emotion of fear may condition illusions. Woodworth distinguishes varieties of illusion. In physiological illusions the illuson is due to the peculiarities of the sense organs and the stimulus is altered by the sense organ. After-images and contrast colours are physiological illusions. Illusions may be due to mental pre-occupation, the mental content at the time facilitating responses which are in relationship to it. Illusions of the response to analogy type are due to making the same response as was made in the past to a stimulus that, in some aspects, differs from the original stimulus. An example of this type of illusion is the cinematograph where pictures appear to change and move, although in reality they are stationary. Here pictures are shown in rapid succession and the same perceptive response is made as if they were actually moving. Again, illusions may be due to insufficient data as when seated in a train and watching another train moving. The stationary train appears to move and it is only when new data is obtained by looking at other objects that the first perception is recognized as an illusion. Imperfect isolation of the relevant fact as in illusory figures and diagrams is a characteristic in the production of illusion.

Pathologically, illusions occur in conditions of emotional stress and fatigue. In the so-called hallucinations of organic sensation, sensations arising from the internal bodily organs may give rise to hypochondriacal delusions but, strictly, these hallucinations are illusions as are the aura of epilepsy. Illusions are found in schizophrenia in which mental disorder misinterpretation is common, in the toxis psychoses and in acute alcoholism in which they may be produced by the suggestions of others.

CHAPTER IV

PSYCHOLOGICAL SYMPTOMATOLOGY IN
MENTAL DISORDER

The doctrine of psychological determinism is the principle of belief that in the psychical field, as in the mechanical field, every event must have a cause. It is the aim and function of psychiatry to elucidate the causes of mental illness, to trace the stages of change from the normal to the abnormal and to lay down the principles of this comparatively new science. Psychiatry, however, displays an inherent and unique obstacle to progress, the psychological difficulty experienced when the normal mind seeks to understand the workings of the abnormal mentality. It is here that a knowledge of the principles of psychology is of outstanding service. While normal psychological processes are still to some degree obscure, psychology provides a method of inquiry into abnormal mental states which is of the utmost value in arriving at a correct assessment of the origin and causation of mental symptoms.

It has been previously seen that the psychogenic theory of the causation of mental illness is largely founded on the concepts of the unconscious mind, intrapsychic conflict and dissociation. The important rôle that affect plays in the production of mental symptoms has been examined. It now remains to indicate the dependence of the principal mental symptoms encountered in mental disorder upon psychological processes and to correlate as far as possible normal psychological processes with the symptomatology of the disordered mind.

It has been stated that mental disorder is a personality disorder and that personality is evolved from the factors of native endowments (disposition, temper and temperament), environmental influences and the type of adaptation made to conflict. These form the reaction-tendencies of the individual. While the two main normal personality types of introversion and extroversion may readily be distinguished the extremes of introversion and extroversion are seen in the psychoses of schizophrenia and manic-depressive psychosis. Here, as would be expected, are displayed the major symptoms resulting from an intensification of the normal personality trends. In schizophrenia, introversion shows itself in a diminution of affective response and in a retreat from reality that may culminate in regression to the elements of the collective unconscious. While the primary defect in schizophrenia is the dissociation of the mind a definite causative factor is the introverted type of personality. From this progressive introversion arises autistic thought and phantasy formation. In the same way the normal personality trait of extroversion progresses in manic-depressive psychosis to extreme extroversion with a marked liability to excessive mood-swing. Four further personality types have to be described. In the hysterical personality (Logre), the constitutional background is characterized by emotional instability an egoistical attitude to life and an inherent propensity to avoid the stress of circumstances by transferring personal responsibility from the individual to those who are in contact with him. This type of personality is selfish, childish and immature and endeavours to evade the necessity for adaptation by evoking sympathy and help from others. It is upon this personality type that the psychoneurotic symptoms of hysteria are evolved.

Pierce Clark described the epileptic personality which some observers state is evident before the onset of epileptic fits. The epileptic personality type is characterized by an immaturity accompanied by intolerance and an overweening self-assurance which compensates for inferiority ideas. Domineering, insubordinate and lacking in moral sense, the epileptic personality shows want of development of the social and group tendencies. A marked religiosity is accompanied by vanity and an absence of self-criticism and of realistic thought.

Since the time of Kraepelin there have been various attempts to define a paranoid type of personality of which perhaps that of Meyer is most generally accepted. Meyer pointed out that the paranoid constitution is characterized by an affect of suspicion, hypersensitiveness and mistrust which culminates in a fundamental inadaptability to community life. Guilt-feelings and inferiority ideas give rise to want of self-confidence and continuous failure of adaptation results in the genesis of paranoia.

The psychopathic personality type is marked by emotional instability, lack of adaptation and an incapacity to learn from experience. There is a psychological immaturity coupled with a defect of moral sense and lack of wisdom which renders the personality not only unable to adjust to the demands of the social group but to continue in repeated acts of delinquency and antisocial conduct in spite of punishment.

It will be seen that personality trends play an important part in the etiology of mental disorder. It is the task of psychology, in the provinces of education and sociology, to evolve methods of moulding and expanding the personality in the early years of life.

BEHAVIOUR DISORDER

Behaviour is a manifestation of mind and it has previously been indicated that, to a considerable extent, behaviour is a criterion of mental disorder. The explanation of abnormal behaviour is found in the psychological factors at work. Behaviour is frequently conditioned by emotional and intellectual alterations which are reflected in mode of mentation and in action. In mental illness, conduct may be entirely alien to the normal behaviour of the individual and is often strange and unpredictable. Conduct impairments may be deduced from physical attitude, appearance, gait and habits.

The following abnormal factors are indicative of special alterations in behaviour. Stereotypy, which means repetition in conduct and speech, is shown in verbigeration (repetition in speech) and in motor behaviour as seen in mannerisms, grimaces and such manifestations as "sentinel" walking. Stereotyped attitudes are evident in the intrauterine attitude, the mummy attitude and the prayer attitude. Stereotypy is common in schizophrenia and denotes regression and retreat from reality. Negativism is another psychological symptom which symbolizes the wish to dominate the environment. In speech, negativism is shown as mutism, in conduct, as resistiveness and mischievousness. Automatic obedience denotes a suspension and alteration in the internal impulses which results in an external stimulus being acted on without personality control.

In echopraxis there is repetition of the actions of others and in echolalia the individual repeats in parrot fashion the words of others. Where all impulses to conduct are in abeyance, a condition of stupor may eventualize in which motor responses are inhibited and normal psychological stimuli have no longer their normal value.

Since changes in behaviour and conduct are frequently the first indications of mental disorder they are of considerable psychological and legal importance.

Attention, which has been seen to be the focusing of consciousnes upon some particular sensation or thing, shows early impairment in mental illness. This morbid alteration in the attentive process is to be expected since the subject of psychological disorder is concerned not with the attributes of external reality but with the mental conflicts which are unconsciously operating.

ALTERATIONS IN THOUGHT PROCESSES

Symptoms arising from disturbance of the processes of thought are the essential psychological features in mental disorder and are uniquely particular to psychological illness since they are evidence of disorder of the entity from which they arise, the mind. Disturbances of thought processes are indications of the degree and extent of mental impairment.

There are two varieties of thought which are normally apparent, realistic thought and autistic thought. In realistic thought the conative impulse proceeds to its goal and in the attainment of its aim is directed by controlled associations and logical processes. Realistic thought is conditioned by fact and not by desire. Motivated by belief, determined by judgment and choice, refined by criticism and the facts of the situation, realistic thought is adaptive thought by which all the circumstances are assessed at their true valuation. Autistic thought, however, while normally serving a useful purpose in promoting planning and future action, may become completely undirected by reality principles and hence does not issue in action but satisfies itself by phantasy. In mental disorder autistic thought is prevalent and with the neglect of reality, gratification is found in phantasy which, in morbid circumstances, results in dissociation. Here wish fulfilments dominate the personality and display themselves in conduct changes and in the evolution of delusions. In this situation thinking is katathymic, determined as it is by unconscious factors.

Further disturbances of thought are seen in the slowing of mental processes, retardation, in the disconnection of speech, the instrument of thought, incoherence, and in flight of ideas which is conditioned, not by logical thinking, but by chance associations of sound and rhythm which result in flight of ideation and in distractability of the attentive process, clang and rhythm association, incoherence and logorrhoea (flow of words).

It has been explained that an idea is a significant mental image which consists of two portions, the image and the meaning. The meaning is supplied to the image by the mind and therefore the image is a psychic-stimulus which evokes the meaning. Added to this psychological process, however, is the particular affect ruling at the time. In mental disorder the tendency for affect to pervade the thought content results in ideas of reference, of influence, of unreality and of obsession, which display themselves as mental symptoms. In ideas of reference a false belief, tinged by emotional tone, motivates the notion that something in the environment has a special meaning personal to the individual. Ideas of reference will, therefore, be seen to be conditioned by affect and one of the commonest ruling affects is that of guilt. Guilt feelings display themselves in the distorted form of persecutory ideas and, as the mental disorder progresses, these ideas of persecution may become systematized in the persecutory delusions of paranoia and other paranoid states. In ideas of influence the individual believes that he is the subject of control by someone or something apart from himself. Hence the evolution of delusional ideas concerned with wireless rays, telepathic thought, hypnotism and the many other controls that the patient thinks are influencing him.

Ideas of unreality are of importance in so much as they typify the dependence of abnormal processes upon normal psychological theory. It has been seen that belief in the reality of the self is dependent upon conation and that the concept of personal reality is essentially conditioned by the exertion of effort. Belief in the reality of things apart from the self is elaborated by the projection of personal reality upon the environment since all striving is against resistance and what resists has force and therefore must be real.

Where the foundations of belief become undermined by disorders of mentality, ideas of unreality may result and display themselves in the psychological symptoms of depersonalization and derealization. In depersonalization the individual feels that he is altered in some way, that the personality with which he is acquainted has changed. This results in a tendency to estimate his personality in a new and abnormal way. This tendency is dependent upon the loss of the impulse of effort and where mentality is dominated by conflict, effort is in abeyance with consequent alteration in the concept of the self. Derealization is similarly conditioned. Here the sense of unreality is projected upon the environment and consequently the surroundings appear strange and unreal.

The genesis of obsessional ideas lies in a defective of apperceptive synthesis. It has been indicated that apperception is the psychological process by which former perceptions are blended with new perceptions which modify the old and integrate the new into the personality. Conduct is influenced by apperception and where apperceptive synthesis is inadequate volitional behaviour is affected and doubt and infirmity of the will (abulia) arises which results in indecision and irresolution. Here failure of apperceptive synthesis may eventuate in that hesitation of intellect that impedes the necessity of taking appropriate action. This condition sometimes called *folie de doute*, shows itself in impulsive conduct and in compulsive acts in which the individual feels compelled to repeatedly think thoughts or perform acts since there is an absence of the feeling of accomplishment. In this condition insight may be preserved and the individual appreciates the abnormality of his condition but is unable, because of the psychological factors involved, to alter it.

INSIGHT IN MENTAL DISORDER

It has been seen that insight is the process of obtaining knowledge regarding relationships. In mental disorder the presence or absence of insight is of fundamental importance. In the legal aspects of mental disorder the presence or absence of insight is paramount and the absence of insight may prove to be a principal factor for certification. Insight, however, strictly involves a capacity for self-criticism and in the overt psychotic individual self-criticism is usually in abeyance. Insight involves an appreciation of the facts and of the methods by which beliefs and actions are motivated. In the psychoses, insight is frequently wanting since motivation of conduct and thought is conditioned by unconscious factors and by their affect. Here the individual's beliefs are impervious to criticism and to argument and his judgment is influenced, not by reason or logical principles, but by the unrestricted effects of affect. Insight is of much importance in prognosis and its possession is a favourable factor in treatment.

AFFECT AND SYMPTOM PRODUCTION

Emotion and mood are included under the term affect. Persistent moods are pathological and moods shows a tendency to find object for attachment and to create objects by the elaboration of delusions and hallucination. In mental disorder affect may be entirely absent as in the apathy of some cases of schizophrenia and manic-depressive psychosis. Affect may be exaggerated in the elation and exaltation of acute mania and general paralysis and may proceed to ecstasy as in some cases of schizophrenia. The feeling tone of euphoria is an effect of mild elation as may be found in disseminated sclerosis accompanied by eutonia, an affect of physical well-being. Affects of sadness, mental pain and depression characterize melancholia and display themselves in rigidity, retardation, inactivity, immobility and in posture, walk and facies. Anxiety, a state of expectancy dominated by fear, is an affect found in asthma, diabetes, exopthalmic goitre and in anxiety states. In schizophrenia, incongruity of affect is marked as would be expected. Here there is marked disharmony between mood and thought. Bleuler named the co-existence of two contradictory ideas or feelings in consciousness ambivalence. Here the individual accepts and rejects at the same time ideas and feelings. Incongruity of affect is also present in involutional melancholia and in paranoid conditions in which there is incongruity between the delusional scheme and the adaptation to the environment.

It has been previously indicated that affect influences belief, doubt and judgment. Judgment is dependent upon proper associations and it is here that affect obstructs the reasoning processes and consequently perverts judgment.

MEMORY DISORDERS

Memory depends upon registration, retention and reproduction. Registration and retention are conditioned by interest, attention and affect. Added factors are the frequency, vividness and recency of the impression. Recognition is an acknowledgment of the fact of previous experience.

In amnesia or absence of memory there is entire memory loss for all previous experience. In anterograde amnesia memory loss is only for recent events. This is usually progressive and is a marked symptom in senile dementia. In circumscribed amnesia, loss of memory is for some particular collection of events which are frequently associated with strong affect. Where physical trauma is involved, loss of memory is localized amnesia and the memory loss is confined to the events immediately proceeding or following the trauma. Instantaneous amnesia may result in complete disorientation as in alcoholism. Illusion of memory is paramnesia, the remembering of false recollections that are, in reality, wish fulfilments. Here the wish is father to the memory. This fabrication of memories is pseudo-reminiscences or confabulation and is characteristically found in Korsakov's psychosis, presbyophrenia, and in pseudologia phantastica (pathological lying). The process of retrospective falsification results in a true memory being augmented by false details and meanings. This is frequently seen in testimony. Another illusion of memory is seen in the *dèja vu* phenomenon where there is a sense of familiarity aroused by seeing or hearing something which appears to be associated with a previous experience. This condition is found occasionally in normal individuals and is common in epilepsy. Excessive retention of memory details is hyperamnesia. Here past experiences are revived with much clarity. This condition is well seen in mania and paranoia. In senile dementia a peculiar memory alteration occurs in cryptamnesia in which the individual relates a story, as new, which he has just heard.

It will be seen that psychological symptoms in mental disorder are symptoms particular to the individual and they must be assessed in conjunction with the personality trends, the environmental factors and the hereditary handicaps that may be present. The process of dissociation, the degrees of intellectual impairment, the quality of insight and the particular implications of affect are predominating factors in the causation of psychological symptoms. Hence mental disorder cannot be attributed to a single cause. A complex of etiological factors are involved each of which plays its part in the evolution of mental symptoms. It is in the mode of individual reaction to the impingement of environmental stresses upon the personality traits and in the manner that the individual deals with internal conflicts that the seeds of mental illness are laid. The maladaptations that are made by the individual are the symptoms and signs of the mental disorder.

CHAPTER V

PSYCHOANALYSIS

As Jones points out, the word psychoanalysis has three different meanings. It may mean a special technique for investigating the deeper layers of the mind and it is also extended to mean the science of the unconscious. In this chapter, however, psychoanalysis is considered as a method of treatment, it is in this context that the word was first used. It is also considered in its more general applications.

Psychoanalysis as a method of treatment was restricted by Freud to the psychoneuroses and particularly to hysteria and the obsessive-compulsive states. Anxiety states, however, are conditioned by psychic causes and psychoanalysis as a therapeutic measure has been applied to anxiety conditions with success.

Factors in psycholanalysis used as a method of treatment are the age, the intelligence and the degree of education displayed by the patient. The factor of co-operation is of importance as is the time factor since adequate psychoanalysis may demand a very considerable length of treatment. In the psychoses, psychoanalysis may be of value in certain cases but here the field is more restricted.

Psychoanalysis uses the method of free association in contradistinction to controlled association as practised by Jung in his word-association tests. Free association practically is based upon endeavours to bring into consciousness unconscious trends and motives and hence to overcome the inner opposition or resistance against self-knowledge. In other words it is the aim of psychoanalytical technique to make the content of the unconscious conscious. The opposition displayed by the mind to this process is termed resistance and since resistance is motivated by the dictates of the superego the unconscious material is always of a nature that is incompatible with the moral, social or aesthetic standards of the main personality. The rôles played by unconscious processes, repression and conflict in the genesis of mental disabilities are, as has been indicated, of outstanding importance. Psychoanalysis as a method of treatment consists in the application of the general principles of the theory of psychoanalysis to the individual. Hence the content of what the patient tells the psychoanalyst is interpreted on the lines of the general theory with special application to the individual. Ideally, the patient comes to appreciate the connection of the repressed ideas with his present difficulties. In practice, the psychoanalyst guides, to some extent, the patient's mental processes towards this goal. In the attainment of this aim the emotion and energy which are attached to complexes are stabilized to their attachment and no longer display themselves as symptoms of mental disorder. Psychoanalytical treatment has a difficult and elaborate technique and amongst its methods, in adition to free association, are dream analysis, the use of transference and predominantly re-education.

During the process of psychoanalytical treatment the relation of the analyst to the patient becomes established by the mechanism of transference. By this process the various affects become detached from their former objects and are transferred to the analyst. The patient therefore reacts to the psychoanalyst according to the affects detached and the analyst occupies in the patient's mind the position formerly held by the patient's parents and near relatives in childhood. Hence the patient dissipates upon the analyst the affects of love, hatred, fear and reverence amongst others which he experienced in childhood and which later became repressed. Here the Oedipus situation is involved and psychoanalytical theory determines interpretation. The process of transference is used by the analyst to overcome the resistance displayed by the conscious mind and is later broken down by the analysis of the patient's affective attitude towards the physician and the affects become associated with their original objects.

By this method conflict is resolved since the energy and affects are no longer divorced from their original objects as the patient has now admitted them to consciousness. Then follows the process of re-education in adjustment and adaptation.

It will be seen that suggestion must play a part in the process of transference and in the guiding of associative factors. The essential mechanism involved in psychoanalysis from the point of view of the patient is the dissipation, during transference, of accumulative affect. This is the process of abreaction, a working-off of the emotional tendencies which are causative factors in mental illness. From the viewpoint of the analyst the essential factor is the terminal analysis of the transference process in its differing aspects.

The application of psychoanalysis to general medicine is seen in the explanation that the psychoanalytical principles have offered regarding the so-called functional disorders. In psychiatry, psychoanalysis has emphasized the essential factors of the unconscious, conflict, repression and the mental mechanisms. The rôle that sexuality plays in mental life owes its recognition to psychoanalytical theory. In the prevention of mental disorder psychoanalytical principles play as yet only a minor part but, with increasing knowledge, psychoanalysis has much to offer in the field of prevention. In the elucidation of the symptomatology of schizophrenia psychoanalyis has achieved portentous results as also in paranoia and in manic-depressive psychosis.

In education, psychoanalytical principles have shown that the teacher occupies to a large extent the place of the parents in the mind of the child, as is seen in the emotional attachment of some children to their instructors. Fundamentally the link between the teacher and the student is one of affect. In learning itself, the questions of affective inhibition and sublimation are dependent upon the reaction of the pupil to the unconscious associations of the subject matter. In the formation of character, psychoanalytical theory states that all character is permanently formed by the age of five, later influences having only superficial effects.

In the study of child life, psychoanalysis has shown the relationship that exists between the child-mind and that of primitive people and has demonstrated the similarity and importance of unconscious thought processes that are common to both, pointing out, in particular, the great differences in types of thinking that exist between the child and the adult.

Psychoanalysis has made important contributions to sociology, anthropology and the arts and, indeed, there is scarcely any department of life to which psychoanalytical theory may not be applied.

CHAPTER VI

PSYCHOLOGY AND PHYSICAL TREATMENTS IN MENTAL DISORDER

Within recent years new concepts have arisen regarding the relationship between psychological and physical processes. This change in viewpoint has been hastened by the evolution of physical treatments in mental disorder and particularly by the results obtained by the use of these new methods of treatment which have implicated physiological factors in causation.

It has been seen that in the theory of interaction it is postulated that the mind uses the brain as an instrument for the carrying out of mental activity. Here the brain may be regarded as the organ of the mind, the physical means by which mental processes find expression. Modern methods of treatment in psychiatry have emphasized the importance of the organic in comparison to the psychological and have played their part in the formulation of the new concept of neuropsychiatry. Previously neurology and psychiatry were considered to be two different entities with definite boundaries and to a large extent differing aims. It is, however, clear that the knowledge obtained from the study of neurological and psychological processes may be amalgamated to the mutual benefit of these two branches. This however, does not imply that all psychological mechanisms may be explained in neurological terms or that neurology is subordinate to psychiatry. It does mean, however, that the concept of psychology must include consideration of neural and organic processes while, in the same way, neurology must concede the psychological factor. Practically neurology and psychiatry impinge upon each other and the erection of rigid boundaries betwen the two subjects leads only to a sterile and inadequate concept of either subject.

Physical methods of treatment in mental disorder are six in number. Malarial therapy, used in the treatment of general paralysis, continuous narcosis and narco-analysis, by which drugs are used for the treatment of states of excitement and as an aid to the release of repressed affects and memories, convulsive treatment, insulin therapy and prefrontal leucotomy. In this chapter the last three methods of treatment will be considered.

It must be emphasized that there are many factors that may influence the final results of mental illness of which a physical form of treatment is but one and that at the present state of knowledge, physical treatments are empirical and governed by results rather than by an understanding of how results are conditioned. It is only by increasing knowledge of the processes of interaction between mind and brain that this experimental attitude will be determined.

CONVULSIVE TREATMENT

The origination of this form of treatment was due to Von Meduna, who, in 1934, used chemical methods to induce convulsions in cases of schizophrenia on the hypothesis of an antagonism between schizophrenia and epilepsy. The results of this form of treatment were poor in schizophrenia but favourable in cases of depression and melancholia.

The induction of convulsions by drugs, cardiazol or metrazol, had several disadvantages particularly in the production of unpleasant affects. In 1938 Cerletti and Bini originated the mode of inducing convulsions by the electrical method in which the technique is simple and secondary symptoms are largely obviated. Although electrical convulsive treatment proved to be of but little value in schizophrenia, in the affective psychoses and, particularly, in mania and depressive states, the results have been outstanding. One of the most important difficulties in this form of treatment is the risk of traumatic complications during the convulsion and curare has been found to diminish the risk of fracture and of other complications. The mode of action of convulsive therapy is still imperfectly understood. While psychological factors have been implicated on the lines of psychoanalytical theory which involves the identification of unconsciousness with death and recovery with rebirth, other theories point to the convulsion itself as the major factor involved since anoxaemia occurs in the convulsions. It is, however, in the comparison of convulsion therapy with leucotomy that a more probable solution may be found. Golla is of the opinion that in convulsion therapy there is a temporary ablation of cerebral cells whereas in leucotomy the disconnection is permanent.

Whatever may be the true explanation, it is clear that in convulsive therapy a physical method of treatment profoundly influences psychological mechanisms particularly with regard to affective manifestations.

INSULIN THERAPY

This method of hypoglycaemic shock treatment was introduced by Sakel in 1934 following his experiences in treating drug addiction by insulin. In schizophrenia, insulin therapy is the method of choice and when combined with electroplexy the results of treatment have been most encouraging. On the other hand, its technique requires experience and the selection of cases for this form of treatment is governed by factors which can only be assessed by those who are practically acquainted with the rationale of treatment. The results obtained from insulin therapy are influenced by the type of personality, the precipitating factors concerned in the onset of schizophrenia and by the degree of gratification which the patient has obtained from schizophrenic mentation. An adequate prepsychotic personality is an indication for a favourable prognosis following insulin treatment.

It is obvious that insulin treatment must have concomitant effects upon biological processes. The fall in the blood-sugar following the administration of insulin, the appearance of coma, the changes in the blood pressure and in cerebral metabolism are factors which still require increased investigation. It is probable that further knowledge regarding brain metabolism will throw light upon the essential alterations in mentality which are necessary curative factors. It is also probable that the autonomic nervous system is a factor of importance both in the origination of symptomatology in schizophrenia and in the effect of insulin therapy.

PREFRONTAL LEUCOTOMY

In the operation of prefrontal leucotomy the inter-relationships of mind and brain are clearly manifested although the mode of connection remains speculative.

Prefrontal lecotomy as a method of treatment of mental disorder was introduced by Moniz in 1935. The essential point in the operation is the division of the central core of white matter within the frontal lobes. The operation severs, on both sides, the thalamo-prefrontal fibres running via the caudate nucleus and putamen (the striatum). When these interior thalamo-cortical fibres are cut it is found that the emotional and intellectual components of morbid thought processes become dissociated, eventuating in an alteration in self-awareness and in self-criticism with a diminution of conflict. Cobb, however, is of the opinion that the operation of leucotomy prevents the spread of stimuli to different cortical areas and impedes association of present stimuli with past memories and habitual responses.

The operation results in a lowering of nervous tension and in the temporary appearance of amnesic symptoms with apathy, disorientation and euphoria. The operation theoretically depends upon the postulates that the prefrontal regions are concerned with the psychological attributes of foresight, apperception of the self and imagination.

These qualities are accompanied by affective tone which is considered to be motivated from the thalamus and from the hypothalamus which are linked with the prefrontal areas by association fibres. Since the operation appears to destroy the faculty of self-criticism the consciousness of the self is in abeyance and its affect is no longer experienced. It has been held (Rees) that the superego must be located within the prefrontal areas and that the id is connected with the thalamus. Hence, when the communications are severed in the operation of leucotomy the superego is no longer able to tyrannize over the id and, therefore, in the absence of self-criticism the deeper layers of the unconscious find expression in mentality and in conduct. The crucial point is the definite amelioration of affective disturbances following the operation. This, however, is accomplished at the penalty of some change in the personality and in the operations of conation, intelligence, memory and insight. Following leucotomy re-education and rehabilitation are obviously necessary since mentality may have been reduced to a "surgically induced childhood" (Freeman and Watts).

The assessment of the results of physical methods of treatment in mental disorder is aided by mental tests of which the Rorschach test and the Babcock series of tests are of value. In measuring the results of electroplexy, Goldstein's tests are in general use while Wechsler elaborated a battery of five short tests which are of assistance in checking the mental results of treatment. Kohs's block test is useful following leucotomy and the Bernreuter personality schedule may be used in checking personality changes.

Indications for convulsive treatment are primarily involutional melancholia and manic-depressive psychosis, but in general, any depressive state may substantially benefit. Insulin treatment has now replaced other methods of treatment for schizophrenia and full recovery rate following this method of treatment is approximately fifty-five per cent of cases treated.

On considering the indications for prefrontal leucotomy it must be borne in mind that the operation is irreversible and that it is performed more from the point of view of ameliorating or abolishing distressful symptoms and modifying conduct than as a mode of treatment of definite psychiatric syndromes. Leucotomy should not be undertaken before other methods of treatment have been essayed. Mental states of fear, anxiety, guilt and persecution, including the obsessive-compulsive states, frequently benefit from leucotomy which may abolish or ameliorate the appreciation of affect.

BIBLIOGRAPHY

Acknowledgements are here made to the following works which have been consulted and made use of in the preparation of this book. Acknowledgments and thanks are also made to Messrs. Bailliere, Tindall and Cox, and to Messrs. Livingstone's, publishers of the author's "Aids to Psychology" and "Catechism of Psychology," for permission to adapt and use passages from these books.

BLEULER	... *Textbook of Psychiatry.*
BRAIN AND STRAUSS	... *Recent Advances in Neurology and Neuro-Psychiatry.*
COLLINS AND DREVER	... *Experimental Psychology.*
CRAIG AND BEATON	... *Psychological Medicine.*
CURRAN AND GUTTMAN	... *Psychological Medicine.*
DEVINE	... *Recent Advances in Psychiatry.*
DUMVILLE ...	... *Fundamentals of Psychology.*
GLOVER	... *The Psychology of Fear and Courage.*
HADFIELD	... *Psychology and Morals.*
HART	... *Psychology of Insanity.*
HENDERSON AND GILLESPIE	*Textbook of Psychiatry.*
HOWE	... *Motives and Mechanisms of the Mind.*
JAMES	... *Textbook of Psychology.*
	Talks on Psychology and Life's Ideals.
JONES	... *Papers on Psychoanalysis.*
	Psychoanalysis.
JOURNAL OF MENTAL SCIENCE	... *Special Number, 1944.*
JUNG	... *Psychology of the Unconscious.*
	Psychological Types.
KLÜVER	... *Mescal.*
KNIGHT AND KNIGHT	... *A Modern Introduction to Psychology.*

McDougall	...	...	*An Outline of Psychology.*
			An Outline of Abnormal Psychology.
			Social Psychology.
			Primer of Physiological Psychology.
Miller	... ...	...	*Types of Mind and Body.*
Myers	... ...	...	*Textbook of Experimental Psychology.*
Pfister	... ...	...	*The Psychoanalytic Method.*
Spearman	... ...	...	*The Abilities of Man.*
Stout	... ...	...	*Manual of Psychology.*
			Groundwork of Psychology.
Titchener	...	...	*An Outline of Psychology.*
Woodworth	...	...	*Psychology.*
Wright	... ...	...	*Applied Physiology.*
Yellowlees	...	...	*Manual of Psychotherapy.*

INDEX

FOR ADDITIONAL NOTES

FOR ADDITIONAL NOTES

FOR ADDITIONAL NOTES

FOR ADDITIONAL NOTES

FOR ADDITIONAL NOTES

FOR ADDITIONAL NOTES

FOR ADDITIONAL NOTES